C000171467

GCN
GLOBAL CYCLING NETWORK

Copyright © Mark Beaumont & Laura Penhaul, 2020

All rights reserved. No part of this publication may be reproduced or transmitted in any form or by any means, electronic or mechanical, including photocopying, recording, or any information storage or retrieval system, without prior permission in writing from the publishers.

Any person who does any unauthorised act in relation to this publication may be liable to criminal prosecution and civil claims for damages.

Mark Beaumont and Laura Penhaul have asserted their rights under the Copyright, Designs and Patents Act 1988 to be identified as the Authors of this work.

This publication was made in collaboration with, and is published by, the Global Cycling Network ("GCN"). The GCN brand is owned by and associated logos are the registered trademarks of Play Sports Network Limited, a company registered in the United Kingdom at 30 Monmouth Street, Bath, BA1 2AP, United Kingdom.

First published in Great Britain in 2020

Cover, cycling, lifestyle and gym photography by Joby Sessions
Cover retouching by Nick Tandy
Mark's 80 Days Around The World photography by Moonsport/Johnny Swanepoel
Transcontinental race photography by © www.jamesrobertson.co.uk
Mark's Cairo To Cape Town photography by © Ant Smyth
Chrissie Wellington photography by © Paul Phillips / Competitive Image / @compimagephoto
Jenny Graham's around-the-world kit photography courtesy of © Apidura

The information contained in this book is provided by way of general guidance in relation to the specific subject matters addressed herein, but is not intended as a substitute for specialist advice. It should not be relied on for medical healthcare, pharmaceutical or other professional advice on specific equipment, psychological, biomechanical, physiological, training, dietary or health needs. The author and publisher are not engaged in rendering medical, health or any other kind of personal or professional services. The reader should take into account personal factors such as your strength and overall health, and consult a competent medical or health professional before adopting any of the suggestions in this book or drawing inferences from it. The author and the publisher, its partners and affiliated companies specifically disclaim, so far as permissible by law, any responsibility for any liability, loss, injury or risk (personal or otherwise) which is incurred as a consequence, directly or indirectly, of the use and applications of any contents of this book. If you are taking medication of any description, please consult your doctor or healthcare professional before embarking on any fast or diet.

ISBN: 978-1-8382353-0-7

-

Printed and bound in Great Britain by Hampton Printing Ltd, Bristol

This book is printed on recyclable FSC (Forestry Stewardship Council) certified paper, which is sourced from sustainably managed forests, produced at a mill and printed by a printer that has been certified to the ISO 14001 environmental standard using vegetable oil based inks, and aqueous based coatings.

www.playsportsnetwork.com

PRESENTS

ENDURANCE

HOW TO CYCLE FURTHER

Mark Beaumont
with Laura Penhaul

Acknowledgments

Mark Beaumont

Thanks to my wife, Nicci, and daughters, Harriet and Willa, for their support and patience during the research and writing of this book, especially all the times I asked the girls to be quiet so I could record interviews! My mum, Una, has worked on all of my expeditions since I was 12 years old and continues to be a huge support. To the entire 80 Days team, across logistics, performance and media, as well as all the expedition teams who've created the rich tapestry of experiences that have been woven into this book, a huge thank you. Well done and thanks to the entire GCN team, led by Matt Skinner, for bringing the book together and cutting down my expansive writing on the topic of endurance to something more bite-sized!

Laura Penhaul

Huge thanks to my partner, Matt Willcocks, for bringing me cups of tea or food in the final throes of writing to meet the deadline, and who didn't complain when he was banished from the house or not allowed on the wifi when we were doing the podcasts. Also, a massive thanks to friends and colleagues that I hugely respect in the world of performance science who gave up valuable time to provide a small insight into their wealth of expertise. Please do follow their podcasts with us and reach out to them individually to deep dive into a particular area to help you go further. And finally a huge thanks to Mark Beaumont, for kindly asking me to come on this journey with him, and to the awesome GCN team – it's been another one to remember!

Foreword

"BECAUSE WE ALL CAN"

Welcome to the second-ever book from us here at the *Global Cycling Network* (GCN): *Endurance*

Following on the heels of our first book, *The Plant-Based Cyclist*, we wanted to move from diet to doing. Creating something that helped everyone – no matter their background or experience – to push their boundaries a little further, to turn that 'What if?' to 'I will'.

So to bring *Endurance* to life and impart his hard-won knowledge, we're very pleased that Mark Beaumont, the acclaimed world record-breaking long-distance cyclist, agreed to step off his bike long enough to pen this book for us.

Mark holds a string of endurance cycling records, the latest of which is for the fastest circumnavigation of the world by bike – all 18,000 miles of it in an incredible 78 days, 14 hours and 40 minutes. This was a record he set in the summer of 2017, and one I had the pleasure of joining him for the very first day of his challenge. Well, I say 'pleasure' but it was a ride that took me well beyond my own personal limits: starting at 4am at the Arc de Triomphe in Paris, I finished some 17 hours later in northern Belgium some 240 miles away. I was completely done but Mark kept on riding for another hour. And he'd continue to do the same for another 77 days or so. Each day, every day, without fail. Quite simply, it blew my mind.

To add further scientific depth to his 25 years of endurance riding experience, Mark has been joined by Laura Penhaul, his performance manager for his record-breaking around-the-world ride and a highly respected elite sports physiotherapist. Outside of her day job, Laura herself is also an endurance world record holder: in 2016, she led the first-ever all-female crew to row the Pacific Ocean – all 9000 nautical miles of it; the story of which you can watch in the documentary *Losing Sight Of Shore.*

"Simply put, I couldn't think of another pairing more qualified to write this book"

Simply put, I couldn't think of another pairing more qualified to write this book to help inspire us all to go that little bit further.

Because we all can.

Si Richardson
***GCN* Presenter**

Si (right) joined Mark (left) on day one of Mark's around-the-world project

WHAT IS GCN?

About Us

WHAT IS GCN?

The *Global Cycling Network* (GCN) is the world's largest and fastest-growing online cycling channel, bringing together a global community of road cyclists who are bound together by inspiring videos, presented by ex-pro riders – from world champions and Grand Tour finishers to Olympic medallists – across *YouTube*, *Facebook*, *Instagram*, the GCN app and beyond.

Every day of every week we create unique, informative and entertaining stories from all over the world of cycling to fuel your passion and knowledge for everything two-wheeled, all with the aim of helping you become a better rider. These include tech advice and know-how, riding skills, entertaining features, riding inspiration, racing and much more.

"We have thousands of cycling videos for you to discover, browse and watch"

On top of our daily new video releases, we also have thousands of videos already published for you to discover, browse and watch whenever and however you want – and all for free. This includes several with Mark such as, 'How Far Could We Ride In 24hrs?' and 'Can We Ride And Survive A Stage Of The 1903 Tour de France?', as well as a stack of other great endurance and bikepacking tips and advice videos.

We've also got videos as varied as how to fix your bike, what not to do on your first sportive or gravel race, and even the weird world of recumbent racing. Need something to inspire you and get your blood pumping, like epic adventures around the world? We've got a lot of that – and more. Much more.

Did we mention that you can also ride with us at our own events and festivals? That we have our own club delivering members exclusive sock designs every month? And our very own GCN app especially for our global community of cycling enthusiasts? Or that you can also find our content in Spanish, Italian, Japanese, French and German as well as English? We didn't? Well, we do and yes you can.

And if you're into racing, we've also created the world's best place to watch and experience pro racing with the *GCN Race Pass* – 100% live and interactive racing, all season-long; the best analysis; no more adverts; by fans, for fans – all in the GCN app. Find out more about *GCN Race Pass* at https://racepass.globalcyclingnetwork.com.

 /gcn   /globalcyclingnetwork  /globalcyclingnetwork   @gcntweet  gcnclub.com

CONTENTS

Introduction:

We Can All Endure p12
Riding A Book Vs Reading A Book p16
Going Beyond Pedalling p20
Culture Shift & Definitions p22
About Mark Beaumont p28
About Laura Penhaul p32
Wise Words: What Makes An Ultra-Endurance Racer? p34

Chapter 1: Planning & Logistics

Plan Your Big Adventure p40
Around The World In 80 Days: Eat, Ride, Rest & Repeat p44
The Four Pillars Of Planning p48
Sponsorship: The Biggest Of All FAQs p52
Wise Words: Live, Move, Cycle: The Logistics Of Endurance p54
Supported Vs Unsupported Cycling p56
Packing For Unsupported Rides p60
Bikepacking Kit For Unsupported Rides p62
Safety Planning: Understanding The Risks p66
Final Thoughts p70

Chapter 2: The Mindset To Endure

The Doorstep Mile p74
Endurance Stories: Climb Like A Grandpa & Summit Like A Kid p76
Endurance Takes Time p82
It's All In The Mind p86
Coping Mechanisms p90
Wise Words: The Confidence To Perform p102
Final Thoughts p104

Chapter 3: Body & Set-Up

Look Back To Ride Strong p108
Pedal Power p110
Cleat Of Choice p116
Body Separation p118
Endurance Stories: Cause Not Effect p120
Common Injuries & How Best To Avoid Them p124
Saddle Health p132

Strength & Conditioning p136
Inflammation – Good Or Bad? p138
Final Thoughts p142

Chapter 4: The Science Of Endurance
Setting Your Benchmark p146
Wise Words: What Defines Endurance? p148
Rapid Recovery p150
The Science Of Sleep p154
Wise Words: The Importance Of Sleep p156
Closing Of The Gender Gap p158
Wise Words: The Female Athlete p162
Final Thoughts p166

Chapter 5: Training For Endurance
Train Hard, Recover Well, Race Strong p170
Programme Planning p174
Periodisation Of Training p178
Reading The Terrain p184
Turbo Sessions & Pyramids p186
Core & Body Conditioning p192
Boost Mobility p194
Wise Words: What Makes A Champion? p198
Do I Need A Coach? p202
Wise Words: No More Tough Love p204
Final Thoughts p206

Chapter 6: Fuelling For Endurance
Food For Thought p210
Get The Basics First Right p212
The Human Machine p214
Wise Words: Eat The Good Stuff p216
Fuelling For Events p218
Sweets & Booze p222
Hydration Matters p224
Going With Your Gut p228
Boosting Immunity p232
A Weighty Topic p234
Wise Words: Relative Energy Deficiency In Sport & Fasted Sessions p236
Final Thoughts p240

"With the right belief systems, planning and training, our bodies have the ability to go further than our minds often believe is possible"

This book will give you the tools to ride longer, whatever your starting point

Introduction

WE CAN ALL ENDURE _

Young or old, female or male, we are all endurance athletes at heart – we can all go further…

MB | **We aren't all built to race Alpine climbs like a Tour winner or** generate the power of a track-sprinting Olympian – but we can all endure. We can all ride further. With the right belief systems, planning and training, our bodies have the ability to go further than our minds often believe is possible.

About 50,000 years ago, we started to communicate with each other and evolve our endurance ability to hunt and travel. About 150 years ago we started riding bicycles and exploring the world on two wheels. This book will explore the toolkit that allows us all to be better endurance animals and, therefore, better bike riders.

Whether turning a 20-miler into a century or a Land's End to John O'Groats ride into a circumnavigation of the globe, how do you create the time and understanding to complete those life-affirming bike rides? This book will help to make your bucket list happen.

I've always been fascinated in that meeting point of where the bike can take you (exploring countries and continents) and what I'm capable of (mentally and physically). Indeed, I've often been criticised for spoiling a good touring ride by going too fast! But having pedalled through more than 100 countries, I now have a new bucket list of places to go back to and explore further. One ambition will lead to the next; you never stop improving and building. Be curious, be ambitious and be a student of endurance riding.

Endurance uncovered

This book includes the frequently asked questions about logistics, mindset and training that I've been asked over the years, with the addition of 'Wise Words' in each chapter from people who I respect on each topic. These sections also act as signposts so that, once you've finished reading *Endurance*, you can delve deeper into these topics elsewhere. *Endurance* is a complete guide insofar as it covers all topics. But I'd never pretend to know it all – I learn something new about endurance every day.

Young or old, female or male, we are all endurance athletes at heart – we can all go further. Improving endurance, in all sports, is about understanding where your biggest gains are in order to get the best out of yourself. The goal may be to break a record or win a race, but I'd prefer to define success in simpler terms in this book – for your projects →

"Origin of the word 'Endure': 15th century, old French, from endurer 'to make hard'. The ability to withstand wear and tear of a difficult situation"

to be successful through sheer smiles, perseverance and great memories.

But here's the catch – a book can only tell you so much. Understanding endurance and becoming a better bike rider can only happen through first-hand experience. You have to live this book as well as read it in order to make it your own and trust yourself as an endurance rider.

Here's the conclusion before we really get started – you have to make this deeply personal, get to know yourself and build your own toolkit, whilst always staying open to change and new ideas.

When I was 12 years old, I bought a Mk1 Ford Fiesta for £60 as a farm car and a *Haynes* manual so I knew how to fix it. I spent countless hours reading that book, then countless days, weeks and months tinkering and thinking, 'Aha, that's what they meant!'

Knowledge is reading and remembering information; understanding is experiencing it. I certainly hope that you understand this book and that it helps you explore the world on two wheels.

Mark Beaumont

Endurance cycling is about moments that surprise and inspire you

Co-authors Laura Penhaul and Mark Beaumont first met through ocean rowing

Introduction

RIDING A BIKE VS READING A BOOK

Get the most out of your bike by getting the most out of this book

MB | **You don't have to be a cyclist to learn from this book. Anyone** interested in going further, planning mini-adventures or major expeditions is welcome to this treasure trove of information. However, as I'm writing this book for *Global Cycling Network (GCN)*, I'll assume that you all have a bike.

Whilst you can read this book in any order you wish, there's a reason we've bolted it together in the chronology that you see on the 'Contents' page. Most people new to the game of endurance would put 'Training' as Chapter 1. You'll see it's Chapter 5. There's a strong reason for this – and by the time you arrive there it should all make sense.

Put simply, most riders think that cycling further is mainly about physical strength and conditioning. This is 'familiarity bias' – athletes (whether amateur or professional) are biased towards the bit they enjoy doing, which is that dopamine hit from exercise.

Many topics in this book could appear in multiple chapters, so if you're looking for something in particular, jump to the 'Contents' section to find it. And always keep in mind that everything covered in this book is interrelated. The mind, the body, the plan. Three words that cover the entire topic of endurance, but there are no silos here. It all connects, so try and think across chapters.

Change through confidence

I think we'd all prefer to be riding our bikes rather than reading a book about it. But sometimes, to improve our ways, we need to hit pause and learn. And learning isn't always about being told completely new things. It's often about remembering things you'd long forgotten, or reflecting on your own ways and figuring out something important from yourself. In any sense of the word, 'learning' is about creating change through confidence and knowledge.

We've failed in our task if you have to be an endurance expert to be able to read this book. This book is designed to be accessible to everyone. →

"This book will help you identify where you can make big and easy gains, as well as how to pull in relevant support and expertise to help you get there"

INTRODUCING

Laura Penhaul

I'm delighted Laura has written this book with me. Previously, I lent on her to put some science behind my ambitions as a bike rider. Now Laura's doing the same as co-author to this book.

Not only has Laura been a physiotherapist through four Paralympic and Olympic cycles, between 2015 and 2016 she led the first female crew to row the Pacific Ocean. This incredible feat took over nine months of physical and mental endurance. I can't think of anyone more qualified to help me write this book.

Laura's passion has always been to bring the methods and rigour of performance sport to the adventure and endurance world. However, that learning is a two-way street, and Laura has always spoken about the mindset and ability to adapt shown by so many endurance and adventure athletes, traits that so many Olympic athletes could benefit from.

In short, big miles make you harder.

LOOK WHO'S TALKING...

MB / LP —

As we've written this book in the first person, except for 'Wise Words', we have put MB (Mark Beaumont) or LP (Laura Penhaul) before each section so at a glance you can see who's speaking.

I've been in that position many times, intimidated by a topic because an expert's trying to show me just how much they know rather than chatting, like you would in the pub.

Real-life riding advice

I grew up loving riding my bike. I started as an adventurer, far more interested in where I'd pitch my tent each night than what my power meter's telling me. However, in the last five years I've pushed the boundaries of cycling endurance, supported by performance teams to break some of the most iconic endurance records, like the 18,000-mile circumnavigation around the world and the 6,000-mile Cairo to Cape Town.

A huge amount of endurance ability is about logistics and psychology. In that sense, endurance is a great leveller – we can all endure. This book will help you identify where you can make big and easy gains, while showing you how to pull in relevant support and expertise.

When it comes to training, there are simple ways to train smarter, not necessarily harder. Knowing what you're training for is key. Is your aim to complete? Or is it to complete within a certain time? Or is it more personal – is it about your own mental and physical health? Being specific about the goal will help you to understand what performance targets you'll need to set yourself. Even that word 'performance' takes some getting used to in the world of endurance – in the good old days people just rode their bikes a long way.

"When it comes to training, there are simple ways to train smarter, not necessarily harder"

Being specific about your goals is key to setting your performance targets

Introduction

GOING BEYOND PEDALLING

Physical and mental endurance is a toolkit you can transfer to any challenge you face

LP | **In the world of professional sport, a wide range of people** with deep expertise are brought together to support individuals or teams to perform in an effort to help win medals. This 'behind the scenes' team is constantly reviewing priorities to ensure focus and input is directed into what'll have the greatest impact on sporting performance.

Not everyone reading this will be training to cycle around the world – although some might! And not everyone will want to break records and ride thunderously fast. This is a book for anyone who has the burning ambition to simply go further. *Endurance* is the broadest of broad churches.

Having worked with Paralympic athletes who'd overcome significant adversity and gone on to achieve their goals, it always made me question why we wait for adversity until we then decide to make the most of life. I wanted to understand my athletes and their mentality; I wanted to feel for myself what it is we draw on when faced with wanting to give up. I'd completed a few triathlons, marathons and 24-hour sportives, but nothing had really challenged me mentally.

In 2011 I heard about ocean rowing and felt that aiming to row the Pacific from America to Australia – 9,000 miles, over 250 days at sea – would be the mental test I was looking for. In preparation for the row I read and researched every ocean rower, reaching out to them to absorb their experiences and learn from their mistakes or successes. This was my introduction to Mark Beaumont. He nearly lost his life and his crew mates when they capsized in the Atlantic during an ocean rowing race to Antigua. A shocking experience but one that became so insightful for our preparations and team selection.

Science behind the stamina

Endurance is a toolkit of mental, physical and logistical preparation that allows you to redefine where you thought you could go. My job is to put some science behind the ambition – and to help translate what Mark actually means when he says 'just keep pedalling' so you can do just that.

The importance for me in this book is to share what aspects of sport science you should consider and apply when planning a goal in the world of endurance, and to use these principles to set you up for success.

Your support network, be it professional input (Laura) or family, are so important

"The importance for me in this book is to share what aspects of sport science you should consider and apply when planning a goal in the world of endurance"

You don't have to be an Olympic athlete to have the same approach to life and to cycling. In fact, you're likely to see much bigger proportional gains than any Olympian when you apply a similar toolkit. We all need an endurance mindset to be successful in life, so why not apply this to becoming a better endurance cyclist as well? When it comes to true endurance, you're far less focussed on raw power and speed – put simply you're building the mind and body to keep going, to be more efficient and not to break down.

Train smarter, not harder and dream big!

The purpose of this book is to help you create those life-affirming rides

Introduction

CULTURE SHIFT & DEFINITIONS

The terminology to kickstart your endurance journey, plus the gear evolution that's sparked a two-wheeled explosion

MB | **When I pedalled my first 1,000 miles from John O'Groats to** Land's End over 20 years ago, the world of the 'tourer' and the 'roadie' felt a million miles apart. Now there's mutual respect and inspiration as these worlds have come closer with many prominent riders even dabbling in 'the dark side', which is simply the other camp from the one you started out in.

"Over 20 years ago, the world of the 'tourer' and the 'roadie' felt a million miles apart"

Governments and national cycling bodies have latched onto this trend with major bike networks adding new segments, especially in North America and Europe. Platforms like Komoot have allowed online communities to grow, helping to make grassroots cycling more accessible outside of cycling clubs.

The phrase 'adventure cycling' in Europe suggests you're planning to leave the tarmac at some point or head to exciting foreign soils; in North America, 'adventure cycling' means endurance road riding and can be closer to home (hence, the Adventure Cycling Association). So, whether you're riding flat or drop handlebars, thin or fat tyres, supported or unsupported, it doesn't matter. What matters is that you're interested in riding further. If so, this book is for you. But for full disclosure, my background is international road riding, ranging from full pannier-bag touring to fully supported racing, so that'll be my bias when writing from personal experience.

'Endurance cycling'

In the avoidance of confusion, because we have a global readership for this book, rather than flitting between saying adventure cycling and endurance cycling, I'm just going to say 'endurance cycling' from now on. Ultra-endurance is just a sliding scale from endurance, so you can decide yourself whether you're a sportive rider wanting to go a bit bigger or an around-the-world cyclist. For the purposes of planning and training, it's all the same.

Professor Greg Whyte OBE, mentor to the likes of David Walliams and Eddie Izzard on exercise physiology, shared with me the best definition that I've heard of endurance and ultra-endurance: 'Endurance is any exercise that →

lasts more than an hour. Ultra-endurance is any exercise that lasts more than a marathon distance, which for a cyclist equates to a century ride.' In terms of physiology and fuelling, the body is into the realm of ultra-endurance long before you might think – cycling around the world is just a multiplication of the century ride 1,800 times over!

We'll talk more about bike set-up in Chapter 3. For now, some broad definitions will suffice.

Evolution of equipment

Semantics can confuse things. We can't just say racing bike or touring bike anymore. Endurance bikes, gravel, cyclocross, hybrid, e-tourer... to name just a few. No-one likes to say the wrong thing for fear of not being 'in the know'. But let's relax about all of that and let's face it – if you're talking about a gran fondo or endurance bike, it's the same thing. And if someone identifies a road bike with a label you don't recognise, it's a safe bet they're talking about a gravel bike of some description. And what's a gravel bike? It's just a road bike with better frame clearance for wider tyres and disc brakes as standard.

This evolution in endurance cycling has been fast. And whilst bike brands have been delighted to jump on the N+1 theory of bike ownership, it's really the cyclists themselves who've led this, changing how they ride and how they pack their bikes.

These days you simply have more choice. In times gone by, British touring bikes had drop handlebars and were made of steel. In 2007 I thought I was being Euro and trendy choosing an aluminium alloy frame with butterfly bars and an internal gearing system. Since then, belt drives, dampening and even the electric option have been introduced for this breed of globe-crossing endurance bikes. But for all the incredible developments in bikes, it's your body and mind that'll make the biggest difference to your endurance.

"We can all agree that frames have become lighter and more comfortable over big miles"

Rationale for endurance bikes used to be that they must be super simple, bikes you could fix with the tools in your back pocket. They had to be metal for the wisdom that you could weld them. But modern alloy frames are so thin and strong that you can't really do that anymore (plus when is the last time you actually tried to weld your bike?!), and whilst you might be a disciple of titanium, steel or carbon, we can all agree that frames have become lighter and more comfortable over big miles.

The same applies to gearing. I cycled the length of Africa – solo and unsupported – using electronic gearing. That's not something you can fix at the roadside. For many, efficiency's become more important than fixability.

While there have been plenty of innovations in the evolution of endurance bikes, the biggest step →

Dialling in your bike fit will maximise comfort and reduce the chances of injury

Endurance cycling stresses your gut, so train using the foods you'll use for your event

"The majority of modern bikes cater for the likes of Mark Beaumont, not Mark Cavendish"

Exploring new landscapes is the key driver for many cyclists' adventures

forward is disc brakes. Mountain bikers have been riding disc brakes for years because they offer more power and better modulation (ability to control clamping force) than rim brakes. They're also more reliable in a wider range of conditions. However, the biggest benefit of disc brakes isn't actually their stopping power on road and gravel – it's the additional tyre clearance they allow. This means you have the choice for much wider tyres, which can increase comfort and grip.

On the roadie scene, disc brakes have been met with some resistance, especially on the competition side of things. But, for the endurance rider, especially when riding solo, the benefits outweigh any downsides including the additional weight.

There are other inspirations creeping in from the mountain-bike world like tubeless tyres and 1x drivetrains. But the heart of the endurance bike evolution is framing. Most road bikes used to employ classic, Euro, race geometry with a negative-slanting or flat top tube and a super-low front end. The drop-handlebar bike market is no longer solely built around these aggressive, twitchy steeds with steep steerers and short stems. Many feature more relaxed, comfortable geometry. In modern times, the bike market is much more segmented – but the majority now cater for Mark Beaumont not Mark Cavendish. That's for those of you who just want to go for long rides and maybe dabble in the dirt.

Introduction

ABOUT MARK BEAUMONT

How Scotland's self-professed 'moderate' cyclist rode his way into the record books

MB | **I've never been a racer. And yet I've always been fiercely** competitive. Who am I beating when I pedal around the world? No-one? Certainly not anyone else. I'm simply trying to figure out my own personal best – but that PB isn't a place you can stay. It changes with time, as ambition and experience give you the toolkit to be more efficient, to go further. Something I figured out a few decades ago is that endurance, by definition, goes on a long time, so you'd better enjoy the process, as well as the destination!

I'm 6ft 3in and 90kg, and quite used to the comment, 'You're a big lad for a cyclist!' I realise that my X factor with endurance wouldn't allow me to do the same within the Olympic velodrome or in a Grand Tour. I'm not the best cyclist in the world – I'm not even the best cyclist in my nearby city of Edinburgh – but I've learnt over the past 25 years, since I was a 12-year-old cycling across Scotland, how to endure.

I was born on New Year's Day 1983 and grew up in the foothills of the Scottish Highlands where my parents ran an organic smallholding. Horse riding and skiing were as big a part of my life as cycling throughout high school. That said, I was only 15 when I completed my first 1,000-miler from John O'Groats to Land's End. I then rode the length of Italy from Sicily to the Alps as a school leaver, before moving to Italy to become a ski instructor. After graduating from Glasgow University, I decided against becoming an accountant as planned; instead, I set out to cycle around the world. The aim? To break the Guinness World Record.

Power of the mind and a plan

Fast forward over a decade and Laura Penhaul was my performance manager for the second time as I cycled around the planet during the 'Around the World in 80 Days' project, where we broke the previous 18,000-mile circumnavigation world record by 37% – but where we broke our own target by 1.44%. This is the clearest example I have of the →

"The desire to win is certainly powerful but can be unsustainable. The desire to better yourself is never-ending"

Chrissie Wellington, four-time Ironman World Champion

In order to inspire you, your challenge needs to take you out of your comfort zone

Life packed neatly onto his bike, Mark racing the length of Africa

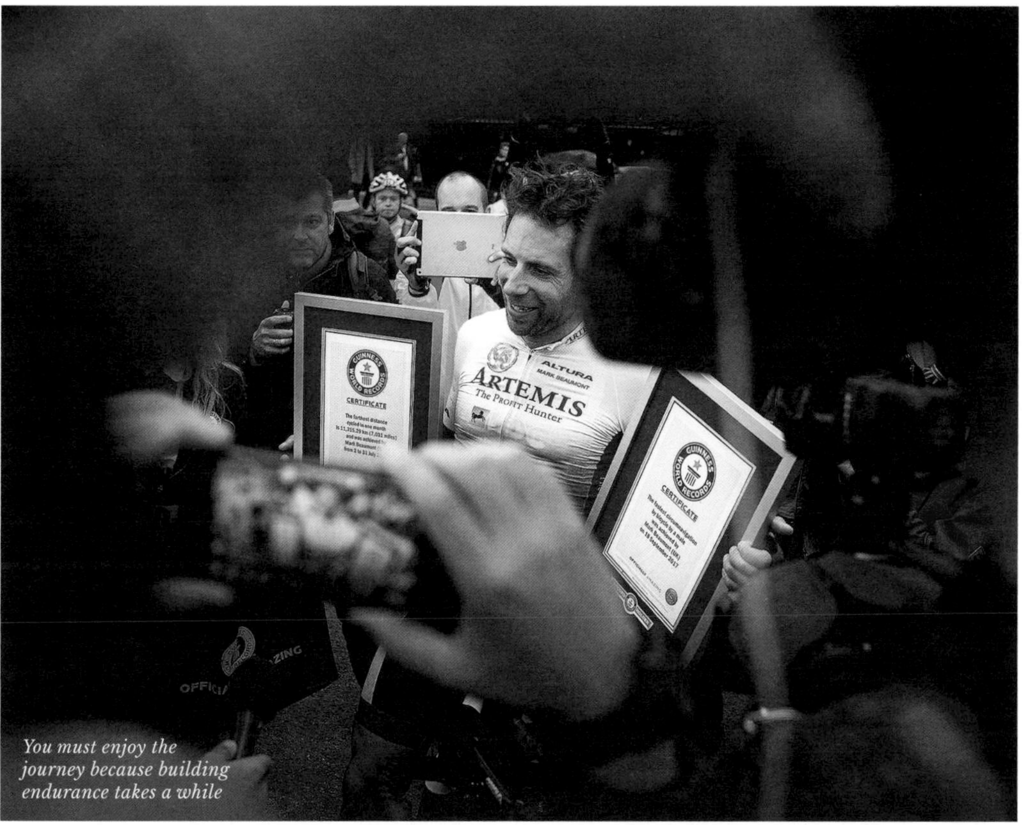

You must enjoy the journey because building endurance takes a while

"We cannot put your readers through the same feat of endurance that you have put yourself through!"

Giles Elliot

power of the mind and the power of a plan. Somewhere in the mix you need to be mentally and physically strong as well!

As a student, I disliked writing and I didn't read much. A 3,000-word essay would take me weeks. A few years after graduating with a perfectly useful Economics and Politics degree – and putting it to good use by cycling around the world – I was asked to write my first book. Cycling around the world sounded a lot easier than writing a book about it. The sheer task of that monumental word count!

Fifteen years later and, having written four books, I've learnt that writing enough is never a problem. Writing concisely is the trick. When I handed in that first manuscript for *The Man who Cycled the World* to my editor Giles (shouldn't all book editors be called Giles?), it was a mighty 205,000 words. I've always tried to keep in mind his response: 'We cannot put your readers through the same feat of endurance that you have put yourself through!'

And with those words ringing in my ears, let's explore the world of *Endurance*.

Introduction

ABOUT LAURA PENHAUL

From a small town in Cornwall to rowing the Pacific Ocean…

LP | **When I set out to row the Pacific Ocean from the US to Australia,** it was about flipping the table and putting myself on the side of the athlete. I wanted to experience what and who I needed to surround myself with to get the best out of myself, the team and the project.

I was born in April 1983, just a few months later than Mark, and grew up at the other end of Britain in Cornwall. My sport of choice was running, taking up cross-country at eight years old. Trewirgie Junior School and Mr Simons, the deputy head, as well as my parents, ingrained in me the beliefs I have today. Our school motto was 'My Best Always' and that's what drives me – to get the best out of myself and others.

Twenty years later, I was sitting on a small rowing boat in the middle of the Pacific Ocean speaking to the children of Trewirgie via satellite phone. I took the opportunity to say that starting from the small old mining town of Redruth, I had no idea where this striving would take me, this hunger to find ways to better myself. Stroke by stroke, shift by shift, day by day, you can continue to move forwards, so never let location, society or expectations limit you.

Activating the plan

Working with Mark over the years, what's fascinated me is his ability to adapt, and his ability to draw on belief and strength in times of difficulty and despair. Is it nature or is it nurture? There are certainly raw character traits here, but also a lot that's been learnt over the decades of pushing endurance goals. By combining Mark's ability to endure, my background in performance support and an amazing team working towards one big scary goal, we built a plan – and then activated that plan – to circumnavigate the world 45 days faster than the previous Guinness World Record.

We had eight months to work together and prepare before the start. And to misquote Ben Hunt Davis, the Olympic rower, every decision was about, 'What Will Make the Bike Go Faster?' For me, that made my job clear – surround Mark in a bubble and reduce the noise around him to maximise his ability to focus on putting consistent power through the pedals.

For this book, my job is similar: to help you focus on where your biggest gains can come from to aid you in achieving your endurance goals, whatever they may be.

Since the 80 Days project, Laura's worked with British Sailing and runs her own business

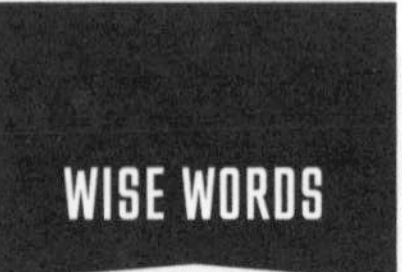

What Makes An Ultra-Endurance Racer?

When it comes to finding your limits, there's no one size fits all

ENDURANCE LESSONS WITH
Ultra cyclists **Jenny Graham, James Hayden** and **Fiona Kolbinger**

Three different athletes, three different personalities, three different backgrounds and three different perspectives. In fact, if you ask three endurance cyclists a question you'll get four different answers. Even in the same field, like cycling, they'll have different training plans, motivations and bike preferences. In conversation with James Hayden, Jenny Graham and Fiona Kolbinger, the individualisation of endurance sport is plain to see, even if all three riders operate in the same sphere – cycling very long distances as fast as they can.

James is the 2017 and 2018 Transcontinental Race winner (the TCR is the cross-Europe unsupported cycling race created by the late, great Mike Hall); Jenny's an ebullient Scot who's pedalled around the planet in record-breaking time; and Fiona's the 2019 TCR victor – and the competition's first female winner.

Nurture not nature

All three are endurance icons. But all three agree that being an endurance athlete isn't something you're born with. 'You learn and teach yourself,' says James. 'Everyone starts out in the same place.' And that place can be emotional. He remembers as a youngster losing his rain jacket on his first long-distance ride and bursting into tears. He had to call his mum for a mental pick-me-up. It's a far cry from cycling 1,800km over the mountains of Kyrgyzstan.

Fiona's start to riding was similarly inauspicious – it took her over a year to realise that you weren't supposed to wear pants beneath your cycling →

"The individualisation of endurance sport is plain to see, even if all three riders operate in the same vein – cycling very long distances as fast as they can"

James Hayden won the Transcontinental Race in 2017 and 2018

Fiona Kolbinger was the first woman to win the Transcontinental Race

WISE WORDS

"No-one becomes an expert at this overnight. The only way forward is through trial and error"

bibs! Lessons are learnt, tears are shed and bums will get sore.

Competence builds confidence

So what scares them about endurance cycling? 'Mechanicals,' answers Fiona. But she learnt. When she brought her bike to the bike shop, she'd always stay to watch it be fixed so that she could learn how to repair it herself.

What scares James most is the 'unknown'. But through experience, his skillset at coping with these situations has evolved and has become a part of his repertoire. Jenny's most frightening experience was her first overnighter alone on a three-day trek. Come nightfall she's in her tent hugging an ice axe, terrified that someone could be out there. There was a wave of relief waking up to find herself still alive and with all of her limbs intact.

For Jenny, as for James and Fiona, adapting to endurance was about building the resilience to cope with the unknown. Cycling is the fun part.

The precept that less is more is universally supported. There's basic kit that you'd bring with you for any bike ride, and different journeys will require specific equipment depending on the length and environment. As well as staying light, you need to leave as much room for water and food as possible. The only thing Jenny adds to the list is a pair of warm bed socks – luxury when it's a freezing-cold night.

Supermarket sleep

As for sleep, James admits to siding with hotels: 'You're going to kip better than you are in a bush, for sure.' Fiona takes the reverse approach and opts to sleep in places that are uncomfortable to hasten her wake-up the next morning. Jenny, on the other hand, says that she'll ride an extra 45 minutes just to make sure she sleeps within a five-mile radius of somewhere serving coffee. There's wisdom in all of these approaches.

When it comes to a bike fit, James swears by one. For Fiona and Jenny? They've never had one! The topic of chamois cream is even more divisive! Fiona's finest piece of advice is simply to try things on your own. Talk to people, ask what they're doing, experiment and find out what works for you.

To hear more listen to the Endurance podcast on Apple Podcasts, Spotify, Google Podcasts, Amazon Music or search for it on your favourite podcast app.

Chapter One

PLANNING & LOGISTICS

Those two words aren't the most exhilarating in endurance riding, but they're arguably the most important. It's time to dial in your preparation

"Bottom-up planning is the ability to know yourself enough to focus on inputs rather than outputs"

Make sure you control the controllables. It'll breed confidence

Chapter One

PLAN YOUR BIG ADVENTURE_

Reaching your endurance goals starts before turning your pedals. As well as a clear dream, you need the roadmap to get there

MB | **'A massive leap in performance takes a quiet confidence in your** ability, a healthy dose of obsession and a bloody good plan.' Words I wrote in my book *Around The World In 80 Days* about how I broke the circumnavigation world record by 45 days. The romantic notion of cycling around the world is that you train like a lunatic, grow fitter than you've ever been, reach the start line and then figure out what you're capable of. The truth is that you figure out what you're capable of during planning and training, write a plan, then read it off script.

Bottom-up planning is the ability to know yourself enough to focus on inputs rather than outputs. What does that mean? It's the difference between what you control and what you don't, and adjusting your performance accordingly.

Scaling back to a day ride, let's think about a 100-miler. Cycling a century is all about focussing on 100 miles. Right? Wrong. 100 miles is an output and will take care of itself. You must know how to plan, pace, fuel and think your way through the ride. This chapter will focus on the first element – the plan. The aim is to flip your event on its head, so that you aren't intimidated by the scale of the task. The distance, the endurance, isn't what you're actually focussed on by the time you reach the start line; instead, you're focussed on your behaviours that'll get you there. You'll be ready to execute the plan, rather than just hope for the best.

I'll elaborate. With endurance, especially in a race setting, your overall distance and time are important – but they're outputs. Understanding what you can affect in the moment, and accepting what you can't, is important.

Learning to sacrifice

When people contact me about their plans to ride long – sometimes a sportive or charity ride, sometimes to pedal around the planet – I never doubt their physical competence. I'll qualify that statement shortly. But, in the 15 years of sharing advice on endurance, I know that many grand plans never arrive at that start line. The biggest hurdle is often being able to afford it – which means the time, money and sacrifices – and realising that the planning and training is what makes the event a success.

Cycling isn't the easy bit – that's not what I'm saying – but the pedalling only happens if you have a roadmap ⟶

"Endurance performance is about how you manage your engine and your mind"

of how to plan a trip properly. In the era of social media, it's more tempting than ever to be inspired by other people's feats of endurance and be inspired to take on your own. Fantastic – that's entirely positive. However, what you're seeing are outputs. What you're not seeing are years of inputs, experience and planning.

Know yourself well

When people tell me about their big dreams, I say two things: 'shoot for the stars' and 'do your apprenticeship'. I'll never tell anyone they can't cycle around the world, but that's not where you start. You need to know yourself well and understand the planning process covered in this chapter. You can know every word of this book, but to become an experienced endurance athlete, you also need to immerse yourself in experiences and make a few mistakes along the way.

There's pride that bike riders have when it comes to 'winging it' – looking like their ride is effortless, that they can fall out of bed and perform at their best. Don't fall into that perception trap. To be the best version of yourself takes forethought. Certainly, when it comes to the big trips, finding the time, funding and team support, plus ticking off the logistical planning, all need to happen before you start turning the pedals. Also, while intimidating, planning should be interesting, involving the sharing of ideas and problem solving. You'll then enjoy a better ride if you do at least some of this big thinking before you start pedalling.

If you've picked up this book, then it suggests you appreciate planning and knowledge, so hopefully no further persuasion is needed!

'You will never do better than what you set out to do.' Why has no-one claimed this quote before now? I use it all of the time. It's an important phrase that's at the heart of planning performance and your ability to build success on your own terms, rather than comparative success, where you're simply trying to keep up with or beat others. This also captures a really important principle of endurance cycling – it's just you and the road.

'You will never do better than what you set out to do' highlights the self-limiting nature of targets, as well as the power of having a plan. Psychological arcs, the power of imagination and other elements that feed into this truth are covered in Chapter 2. When it comes to endurance cycling, even if you're in a race, the only person you're really competing with is yourself, trying to figure out what's sustainable and what your personal best is. This isn't about drafting, your sprint finish or even your bike handling. Endurance performance is about how you manage your engine (nutrition and conditioning) and manage your mind (suffering and focus).

Mark and Si Richardson (right) completing the North Coast 500 in three days

Break your challenge down into chunks to raise prospects of success

Chapter One

AROUND THE WORLD IN 80 DAYS: RIDE, EAT, REST & REPEAT

Time in the saddle, rather than seeking top-end speed, should be at the heart of your endurance planning

MB | **You don't have to cycle around the world but let me use that as** the example for how to plan any complicated endurance event. When we set the circumnavigation world record in 2017 – an 18,000-mile effort in 78 days, 14 hours and 40 minutes – it was based on a plan of 75 days' riding, three days of flights and two days of contingency. I ended up using 14 of those 48 hours of contingency, breaking the previous world record by 37% and hitting our target by a margin of 1.44%.

With due respect to New Zealander Andrew Nicholson, who held the previous Guinness World Record for the fastest circumnavigation by bicycle, mine was not a like-for-like attempt – I was fully supported and he wasn't. But the fact remains, you can't target 123 days, to come home in 78 days. Over two-and-a-half months, you're so sleep deprived and suffering constantly that you can't make it up when you've got to average 240 miles a day. To come home in 78 days, you have to plan to come home in 78 days, which is what we did.

As an ultra-endurance rider, you go to a place that I call 'idiot mode', meaning your headspace and thought processes become so narrow that having a thought of what jacket to wear is an almighty effort. My point is, if you've already done all the thinking, you've pre-written the script; when it comes to the event, all you have to do is keep the wheels turning.

Ride on time

The most commonly asked question as I pedalled across the world was, 'Where are you aiming to reach today?' My answer was always the same: '16 hours!' I can't control the quality of the roads – which were variable in some parts of the world, to say the least – and I can't control the weather, but I can control the time I'll spend riding. And I know if I ride more than 16 hours, I don't recover sufficiently to do the same tomorrow.

This might sound very obvious – but is it? Most riders aim to cover an average mileage. My average mileage had to be 240 miles. That's not your best day – a day that'll live long in the memory →

"Don't let your ego talk you into writing cheques that you simply can't cash"

for just how far you rode – that's your average. You can't make it an average unless you're willing to cycle through it consistently. The mind isn't strong enough (when it's in idiot mode) to understand the power of long-term averages. If you smash that average one day, complacency can quickly creep in. If you can't reach that mileage, you become downbeat and push it too hard, risking injury. It's important to practise, to know your mindset in those moments will be different from in training.

The long-term average and the race will take care of itself if you take care of inputs. If we 'faffed' for five minutes every time I got off the bike, that'd have added a day to the world record. A 210-mile day was just as important as a 270-mile day, assuming I'd done the same thing – cycle, eat, sleep, repeat.

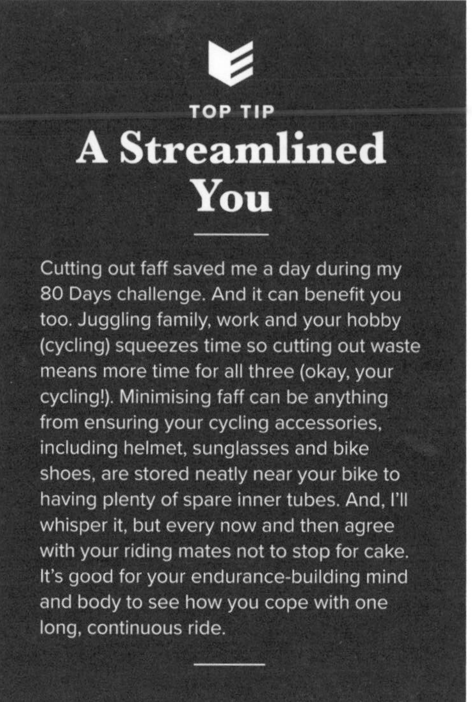

TOP TIP

A Streamlined You

Cutting out faff saved me a day during my 80 Days challenge. And it can benefit you too. Juggling family, work and your hobby (cycling) squeezes time so cutting out waste means more time for all three (okay, your cycling!). Minimising faff can be anything from ensuring your cycling accessories, including helmet, sunglasses and bike shoes, are stored neatly near your bike to having plenty of spare inner tubes. And, I'll whisper it, but every now and then agree with your riding mates not to stop for cake. It's good for your endurance-building mind and body to see how you cope with one long, continuous ride.

Importance of testing

Through testing we figured out I was capable of riding four-hour sets before needing a break. I could ride longer, but this was about figuring out what was sustainable long term. I'd need to start at 4am in order to finish at 9.30pm with 30-minute breaks. Setting my alarm for 3.30am and assuming an hour to eat, admin and recovery at the end of the day for 10.30pm bed meant five hours of sleep. No matter how you break up your day by shifts on the bike and recovery/ sleep patterns, you need to test this.

Most cyclists overestimate the average speed they can cycle, but underestimate how far they can travel. Suggesting a 15mph average speed might sound pedestrian, but experienced riders will tell you that this is a solid effort. When it comes to your endurance challenge, don't let your ego talk you into writing cheques that you can't cash. Ultra-endurance races are won through great administration and ruthless consistency. That's how we ended up splitting an 18,000-mile race into those four-hour blocks.

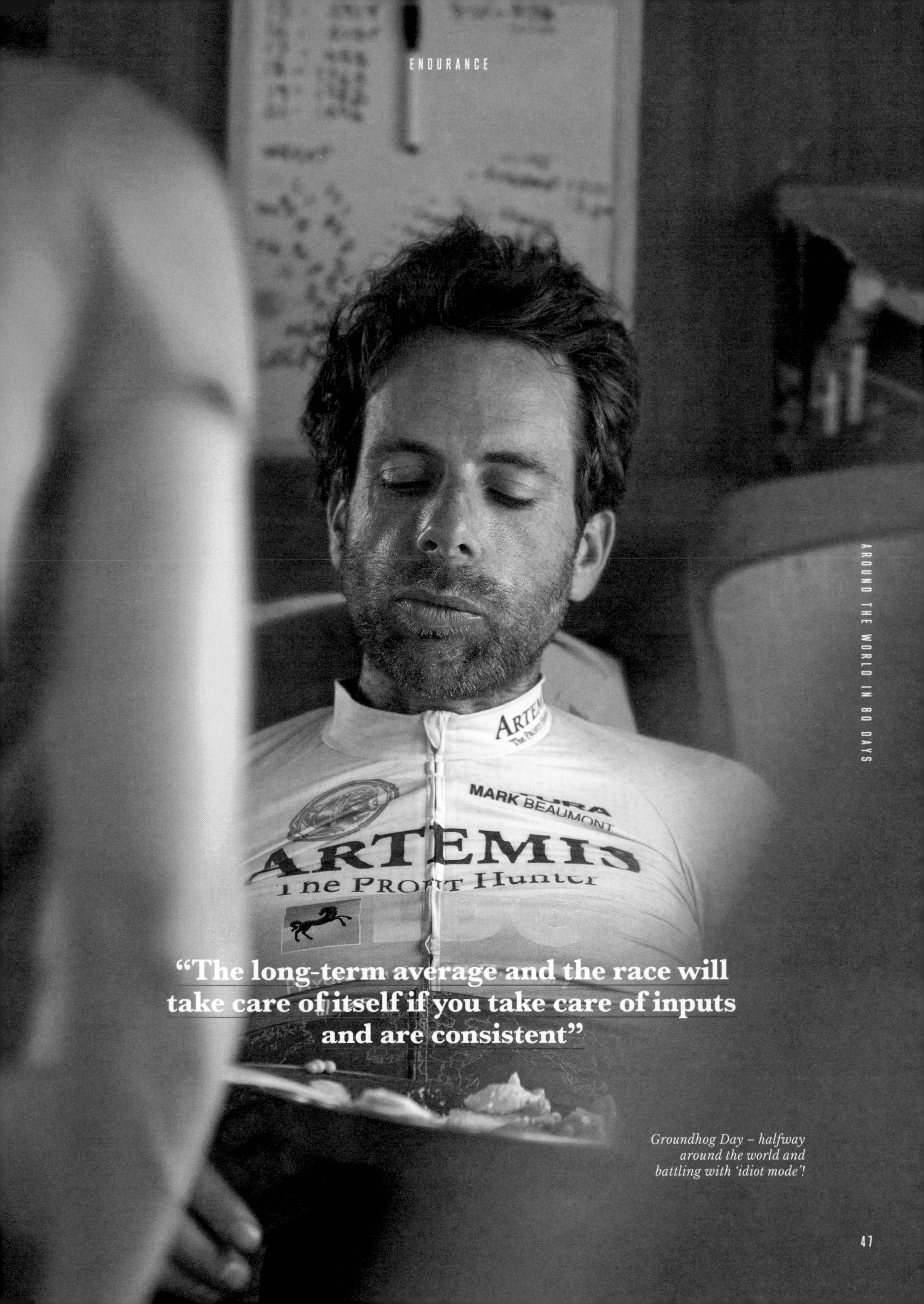

"The long-term average and the race will take care of itself if you take care of inputs and are consistent"

Groundhog Day – halfway around the world and battling with 'idiot mode'!

Chapter One

THE FOUR PILLARS OF PLANNING_

When it comes to challenges that are imagined and created by you, there's a helpful process to make it more manageable

MB | The Four Pillars of Planning are suitable for any feat of endurance that'll require more than just your physical training to take on. This doesn't include events like a sportive ride where the bulk of planning is done for you. This is for endurance projects that you both create and then take part in. You can adapt the following sections to your specific plans, but they're designed to be applicable equally for charity events to record attempts, from a single day to a multi-year.

As mentioned in the introduction, we all have a familiarity bias. In the case of endurance challenges, this is the desire to focus on training and physical preparation (jump to Chapters 5 and 6 for a deep dive into how to be a better endurance bike rider). However, if you're planning your own project, as opposed to entering an organised event, skip this chapter at your peril.

Be objective over your big plans for a few minutes – what is it going to take to be successful? Write those words down. They're likely to fall into these four categories: athlete, logistics, affordability, media. Training will be one word ⟶

The four pillars of endurance projects are...

Athlete(s)

Topics of training, bike fit, nutrition and lots more that'll be covered in later chapters. Dare I say, these are the topics that most people spend nearly all their time on.

Logistics

Crewing, supplies, mapping, route quality and topography, kit choices, weather and climate, tracking, risk assessments including contingency planning and so much more.

Affordability

Having the time, before and during, as well as the money to pull off the plan. These include budgeting and contingencies, sponsors and other people around you who are needed to make the plan a success.

Media

You might have charity elements, educational partners, social-media obligations, and photography and filming needs that impact on logistics and timings, as well as levels of professionalism to consider as projects scale.

"What needs doing most is rarely the same thing as what you want to do"

Use time on long training rides to brainstorm, then write down new ideas when you get home

Ultra riders like Jenny Graham succeed through planning and actioning

STORYTELLING
LOGISTICS
PERFORMANCE
FILMING
PHOTOGRAPHY
BASE CAMP ADVISORS
SOCIAL REACH
WEBSITE
BRANDING
WEATHER
CLIMATE
ROUTE
OPTIONS
NUTRITION
TOPOGRAPHY
PERIODISATION
BIKE
FIT
HYDRATION
WIND TUNNEL
TEAM SELECTION
MEDIA
COACH + ONLINE
COMMS
TIME LINES
ENDURANCE
BIKE CHOICE
FAMILY
RISK?
HOSPITALS
MOBILE COVERAGE
STRENGTH
TRAINING
BUDGETS
TEST EVENTS?
KIT
ELECTRONICS
CONDITIONING
FIRST AID
SCHOOL LINKS
SPONSORS
APPAREL
CASH
CHARITY?
TALKS

Your word map is the start of the process of organising your thoughts

of many on the page. You can doodle a word map, like above, or organise this as a mind map. Now be objective about your motivations – what will you prioritise? What needs doing most is rarely the same thing as what you want to do. It's harder to pick up the phone to would-be sponsors or sketch out a communication plan. Be aware of this bias and put structure into your diary so that you focus on the parts that need to happen.

The importance here is to not just have the big physical event on your horizon and then 'stuff' that needs ticking off in a hap-hazard manner beforehand. Without priorities and focus, the likely result is that the scale of the task will grow increasingly intimidating – and you'll end up cramming in the final weeks.

Conserve energy by planning

I made this mistake the first time I cycled around the world in 2006/07. I was so run ragged by the time I arrived at the start line in Paris that the excitement propelled me as far as Charles de Gaulle airport, on the north east of the city, before I had to stop for a double espresso and sit down as I was falling asleep. I was less than 50 miles into an 18,000-mile race! Being tired, with a suppressed immune system on the start line, is a common mistake. We can do our physical self a huge favour by how we approach the logistics behind any endurance event.

Chapter One

SPONSORSHIP: THE BIGGEST OF ALL FAQS _

Key to securing assistance for your endurance challenge is ensuring that your values match those of your potential sponsor

MB | **Is your event an entirely personal challenge? If so, crack** on. All you need to focus on is the first two pillars of the planning equation – Athlete and Logistics. But the thing I'm asked more about than anything is how to raise finance and gain sponsorship. Most big dreams don't get to the start line because people can't afford the time and cost. If I was given $100 for every time someone asked me for advice on sponsorship, I wouldn't need any myself!

Find common ground

So the tone of correspondence with potential sponsors and media partners is crucial. I suggest you have a 'quiet confidence' – which means you don't overstate your ability – but you need to reassure them that you'll see this through.

Which brings us to shared values. Your job in having a sponsorship conversation is to shift the 'lens' that you're looking at the proposal from 'cost' to 'value'. The difference? Before we talk about money, a brand or business is only going to work with you if you complement how they want to be seen in the market.

What's the middle ground between you and them? Just look at the mission statement, values and marketing of the business. Do your plans and who you are fit well with them? For my 80 Days sponsorship, the values included...

— **Global ambition and media reach.**
— **Creating leaps in performance and being entrepreneurial.**
— **A diverse performance team.**

This approach also allows you to break down the barriers between commercial and corporate sponsors. Commercial sponsors are those from cycling who are already connected to your ambitions, but likely to be approached regularly as they're the obvious targets. Corporate sponsors are those who have no connection to cycling. It's how I've ended up being sponsored by everyone from plumbing companies to fund managers.

The key message from this section is to flip your proposal around. It's obvious why you care and think your plans are important. But why would other people care? If you can answer that question thoroughly, but succinctly, then you can start to build some great partnerships.

Share your story – don't assume the comms will happen automatically

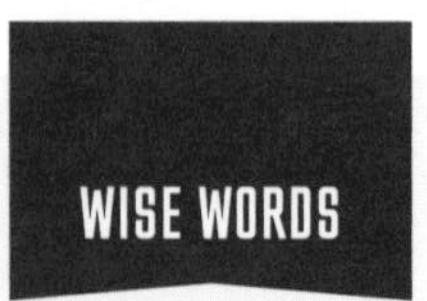

Live, Move, Cycle: The Logistics Of Endurance

Expect the unexpected and plan for every scenario; in fact, do what the military would do

ENDURANCE LESSONS WITH
Mike Griffiths, Mark's logistics manager for Around the World in 80 Days

Logistics boils down to the adage: 'Who? What? When? Where? Why?' As a snapshot, where am I going? When will I finish? Why am I doing this? Mike's advice is to ask yourself these questions before you set out on a ride and write them down.

From the beginning, the British Army drilled into him three principles essential for the success of a project: **Live, Move, Operate**.

Live refers to your health and wellbeing. To achieve an objective, you must ensure that you get to the end of it in one piece.

This is where **Move** comes in. It refers to the logistical questions related to transporting X from A to B. That means knowing your routes and your timings.

Finally, **Operate** refers to the mission. That could be anything from riding your bike, building a trench or heading out on a hike. When planning how to accomplish the project, it's essential to take every precaution to operate unhindered. It might sound obvious, but if it's obvious that means it's important.

Live, Move, Operate is the essence of logistics. Every decision falls into one of these categories.

"When planning the project, take every precaution to guarantee that you can operate unhindered"

To hear more listen to the Endurance Podcast on Apple Podcasts, Spotify, Google Podcasts, Amazon Music or search for it on your favourite podcast app.

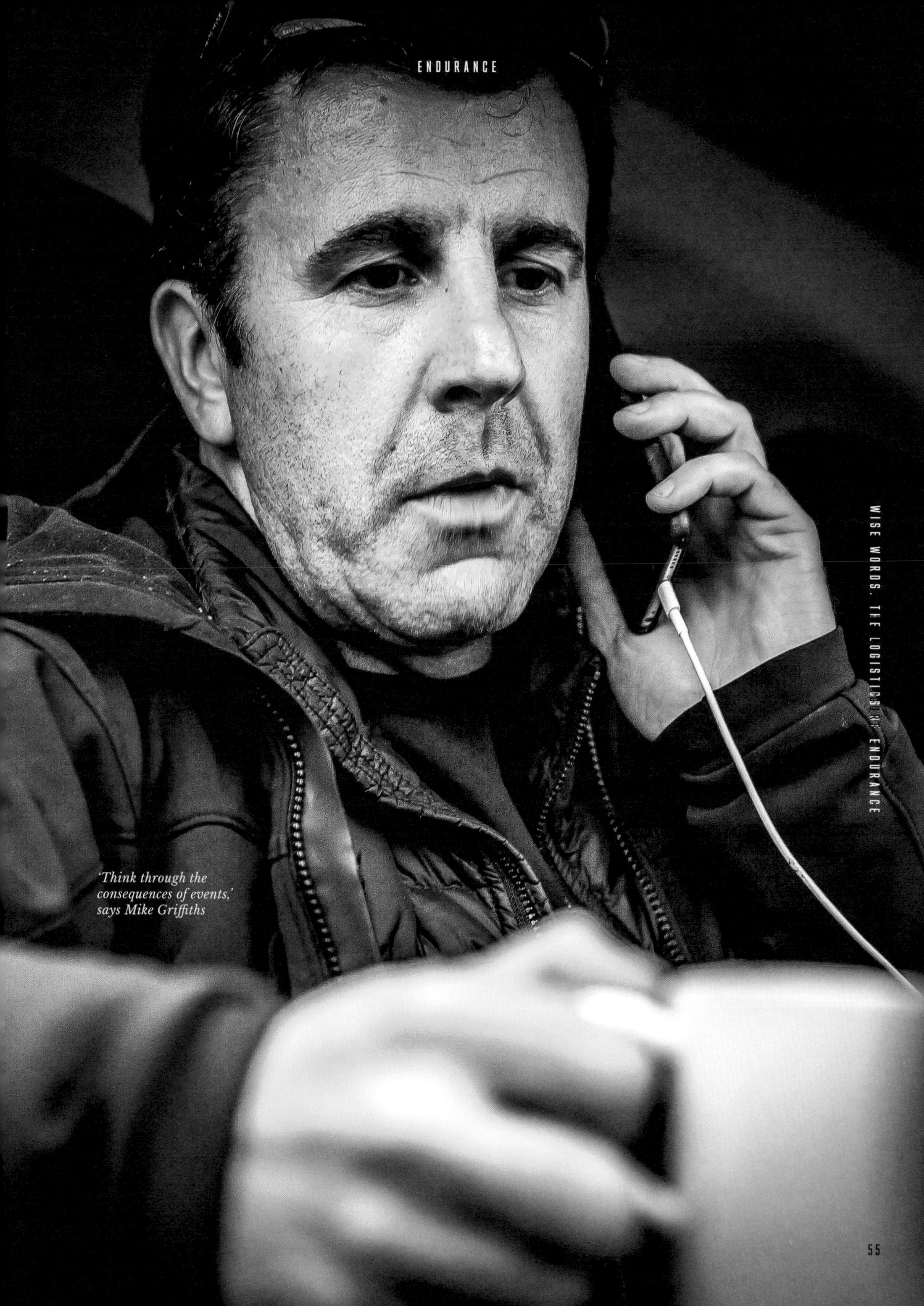

'Think through the consequences of events,' says Mike Griffiths

Chapter One

SUPPORTED VS UNSUPPORTED CYCLING

Mark's conquered challenges both solo and with a big team behind him. So how do they compare?

MB | **If you have a choice to make, run through the pros and cons of** riding supported or unsupported. When you're supported, you carry less kit and have someone looking out for you. When it comes to the likes of Guinness World Records there's no distinction, so it boils down to whether you want to be 'pure' about the racing and opt for supported, or 'pure' about the adventure and opt for self-sufficient.

For both unsupported and supported, there are extremes. Take the 2020 GBDuro – a 2,000km bike-packing race the length of Britain where riders had to carry their own food for the entire course. It's unsupported in the extreme when you can't even stop at a garage for food! At the other end of the scale, my Around the World in 80 Days project had about 40 people involved across logistics, performance and media. At any one time on the road we operated a two-vehicle support system. These had a crew of six people onboard, including a performance manager, a logistics manager, a mechanic, a cook and two camera crew.

Very different challenges

I've completed many unsupported as well as supported endurance rides, and they provide a different headspace. In one sense your life's easier when you're fully supported. In another, it's not just about you. Never underestimate how tiring and stressful the support roles can be, and always remember to acknowledge and thank them. Don't underestimate how intense this relationship can become. You're living in close confines and often lacking sleep.

"Causing tailbacks whilst supporting cyclists promotes dangerous driving from other road users and puts the cyclists in further danger"

It takes an experienced support crew to avoid being emotionally tied in to how the cyclist is feeling. Also, make sure that everyone understands their own roles, and the boundaries that exist between roles, so the crew don't end up upsetting each other. This is extremely important for all involved. →

Learning to trust yourself is a key part of unsupported riding

Never underestimate how tiring the support roles can be

Driving in support roles is an enormous topic, but to keep it simple your role is to stay within a pre-agreed distance of the cyclist/s, depending on how self-sufficient they are. You'll be paying closer attention to the cyclist

"Remember the golden rule of support – you can only look after the cyclist if you first and foremost look after yourself"

who's carrying nothing, for instance, than the one who has their own snacks and repair kit. Ultimately, your responsibility when driving in support is your own safety and to stick to the rules of the road. You must remember that cyclists are absolutely responsible for their own safety.

If you have to pull over, make sure you're clear of the road edge so that the support crew can walk around the vehicle without stepping into the road; always wear fluorescent clothing when in support roles; and never stop at the bottom of hills, as cyclists won't want to stop there or be handed food before a climb.

If riding in hot climates, take care when parking on verges as catalytic converters can set fire to dry grasses. And beware of muddy verges after a heavy downpour. Remember the golden rule of support – you can only look after the cyclist if you first and foremost look after yourself.

TOP TIP

A Family Affair

Having those close to you on-board with your challenge will increase your chances of reaching your goals. For example, explain to friends that your Friday-night session at the pub will be replaced by a glass of wine (or water!) as you have a long ride in the morning. Between the banter, they'll soon become a great source of encouragement!

And plan it with your family so that your training doesn't come at the expense of them. This can be a tricky balancing act but engaging them from the start will pay dividends in the long-term – for you and them.

However, if you're making changes in your lifestyle, which are things that your closer friends and family don't do themselves, then be aware that you might be met by concern or doubt. For example, a non-cyclist would worry about an endurance ride, night-riding or safety in traffic. So it's important that as you build your ambitions, you have 'mentors' – people you can communicate with outside of your close bubble, who provide reassurance and feedback.

Families always come first, but families are so emotionally connected to you that they'll often tell you all their fears and insecurities, which you then have to take onboard and balance with your hopes and dreams. So if you have ambitions in endurance, you need to make sure your friends and family are along for the ride, but if they aren't endurance bike riders themselves, that you have communications outside of this close group to keep the fuel in your fire, whether that's a coach, riding buddies or even social media support from peer groups.

Your bike will become your mobile home so you must be organised

Chapter One

PACKING FOR UNSUPPORTED RIDES_

Your mobile home maximises every ounce of steed space for the essentials of shelter, warmth and fuelling

MB | **If time's no object on a multi-day or week ride, then a more** traditional touring set-up might give you the space that you desire, whether that's the full five-bag regalia or a simpler three-bag arrangement. However, I'm assuming that most will be interested in a bikepacking set-up with handlebar, frame and seatpost bags to optimise bike handling and endurance capacity.

The handlebar bag's the hardest to access during your day's riding, so should be seen as your 'house', containing your roll mat, sleeping bag and bivy bag or tent. If you have a poled tent, separate the poles and fit in the frame bag. I either use an airbeam tent that's inflated using my tyre pump or a bivy bag. Many riders pack a thinner sleeping bag than the weather requires, knowing they'll sleep in their warm jacket (choose PrimaLoft over down if likely to get wet or humid). Your seatpost bag's your biggest space and should be packed with your stove and pan, plus spare clothes and spares for the bike. Secure tightly to stop it swaying when riding. One way to avoid this is to use a Tailfin or similarly light frame.

"The handlebar bag's the hardest to access during your day's riding, so should be seen as your 'house'. It's where you pack your roll mat, sleeping bag and bivy bag or maybe your tent"

Hints for longer tours

Wrap a decent amount of electrical tape and strong tape (like Duck) around your downtube. You barely notice it, and it can be unwound and used for fixing holes in bags, patching the inside sidewall of a tyre or other running repairs. A couple of cable ties and small compression straps are also very helpful for breaks. And always pack spare bolts for your cleats.

Your packing will depend on the climate and regularity of supply points. Some tours you may decide to do away with the stove and buy food as you go; others you'll need to be entirely self sufficient, bringing chlorine tabs or a water purification system if you're unsure of the water quality from streams and taps.

Chapter One

BIKEPACKING KIT FOR UNSUPPORTED RIDES _

You'll need an array of bike bags, plus bike-specific tools, to keep you riding strong and smooth

MB | **You should leave space in your bags for food supplies. Gravel** and road bikes handle well with bike-packing bags, but be aware that steering will feel different until you get used to it.

Luggage

Frame bag These are half or full frame – make sure you choose the correct size to fit under your top tube – and, if chosen, test what size water bottles you can carry in half-frame bags, especially on smaller bike frames. Try to avoid an endurance ride with anything on your back.

Seatpack This is where you can fit most of your kit. If you're carrying a GPS tracker, I clip this onto the top of the seatpack. Opt for a brand that has bungee cords or straps on the top, so you can stash rain jackets without having to stop and open bags.

"Try to avoid an endurance ride with anything on your back"

Feedbags These remind you to eat regularly and are pouches that should be attached near the stem of the handlebar.

Handlebar bag Make sure your bars are wide enough for a packed bag, which will have your tent or bivy, sleeping roll (half size if you're going ultra lightweight) and sleeping bag. Many gravel bikes have 44cm- or 46cm-wide bars, as opposed to standard 42cm road bikes. This extra width's great for bike-packing bags.

Top-tube bag Mobile phone, money, anything small you want to grab quickly.

Kit list

Tools/repairs Multitool, pump, spare tube, sealant if you're riding tubeless, patch kit, spare derailleur hanger, quick link for chain (make sure you have the right size as they differ for 10-, 11- and 12-speed cassettes), tyre levers and two 700ml or 24oz water bottles. Bikepackers often carry a bottle in a food pouch on their handlebars, which reminds them to drink, as well as being a convenient place to carry if your frame triangle's packed. However, you may be limited to a smaller bottle on the seatpost tube of your frame when riding with a frame bag.

Optional extras Two CO_2 cartridges (for rides where speed is important), valve core remover, Presta-Schrader adaptor, chain lube, extra brake pads and super glue. →

Wider, flared handlebars afford space for a bar bag without losing hand positions

The gear Jenny Graham used when riding around the world

"Avoid taking ibuprofen on endurance rides as they're harmful to your kidneys"

Clothing

Two pairs of bib shorts as salt sores and a wet chamois are best avoided by changing. One or two cycle jerseys. Merino wool is popular, as it doesn't pong as much as Lycra. Sometimes I wear road Lycra jerseys when bikepacking, especially if it's mainly road as opposed to gravel. Leg and arm warmers; two pairs of socks; rain jacket with a hood for comfort; rain shorts or pants is optional depending on where you're going. Mitts and/or gloves; PrimaLoft vest or jacket (a thin, lightweight but warm overlayer); for women a good sports bra is essential; waterproof overshoes (thermal if needed) or you can use waterproof socks or plastic bags in your shoes if it's not too cold; helmet; and, if riding on singletrack, a headlamp. Off-bike trousers or shorts – opt for trousers in Scotland or Scandinavia in the summer to keep the midges and mosquitoes away. A woolly hat's wise in cooler climes.

Electronics

20,000maH power bank, or whatever size you can carry that's compact and light. Phone, charger and earbuds. Cycle computers; a micro-USB charger and USB plug; lights – if possible, take two rear lights and always leave one blinking, even during the day. It makes you more visible to passing traffic. Also, pack chargers for these, plus headtorch and spare batteries, GPS locator, spare batteries for power meter and camera (stills/action). And remember your charger if riding with electronic gears.

Medical

Suncream, chapstick, paracetamol. Avoid taking ibuprofen as they're harmful to your kidneys, which are already being worked hard. Replace with patches or a gel. Personal medication and anti-histamines. Caffeine tablets if you're doing all-night rides. Sunglasses (ideally with photochromatic lenses. Lens tint changes depending on light conditions); toothpaste and brush (folding); chamois butter/cream; saline solution to wash out wounds and for contact lenses, plus spare lenses; water filters or chlorine tablets; plasters; if needed, mosquito/midge repellent; and don't forget toilet roll!

Personal

Stove, pan and mug, windproof lighter and spoon. Pocket knife, bank cards and a little cash. When I rode the length of Africa, I asked my mechanic to design an expanding bung for inside my seatpost, so I could hide $250 cash, plus photocopies of my passport and visas. If I lost my wallet and passport, as long as I had my bike and a 5mm Allen key, then I had my secret stash! I'd also recommend wet wipes; a headnet to fend off midgies or mosquitos; tweezers; lip balm; a spare ration pack; multi-vitamins to keep you strong and healthy; paper maps; and, to finish things off, your country's flag to stick on your bike or helmet!

Chapter One

SAFETY PLANNING: UNDERSTANDING THE RISKS _

When it comes to bikepacking, you must think through safety rationally and don't just hope for the best

MB | **On any ride, these are basic ideas to plan for an incident: a spare** inner tube, patches and pump, plus a magic link in your chain (small connector if chain breaks); having a wind and rain layer, even for when you least expect the conditions to change; and having contingency food for if the ride takes longer than planned. Let's assume these basics don't need to be explained further.

When planning longer endurance rides and multi-day trips, it's vital that someone else knows your plans and you have a twice-daily check-in system. Even a text message or a social post or a tracker update – just something that tells someone that you're doing fine. If these updates aren't sent, you need to have a process in place for what happens next. You could agree to a six- or 12-hour grace period, during which time you can get in touch without anyone sounding the alarm. However, ensure they're aware that this time period should shorten if you're in an area of higher risk.

"When planning longer rides, it's vital that someone else knows your plans and you have a twice-daily check-in system"

Communication is patchy in remote parts, though many affordable GPS devices can track and send your location using the geostationary satellites. But even this system can be flawed so before embarking on a major ride, check the mobile coverage map of your service provider and also check the satellite coverage if you're carrying a GPS device. I've often used a SPOT tracker (satellite safety device), which features an SOS function that pings to predetermined text or emails.

Protect from crashing

The greatest risk by far to any cyclist is a crash. So, ride defensively, especially if you're abroad and don't know the road culture; wear mitts, as your hands are almost always the first part of the body to hit the ground; and always wear a helmet on busy roads and descents. I'm not going to enter into a debate about always wearing a helmet, as while I've worn a helmet in recent years on expeditions, that wasn't always the case.

Outside of crashes, think about risk in terms of 'exposure', which →

Check out mobile-coverage maps and invest in a GPS tracker for solo endurance

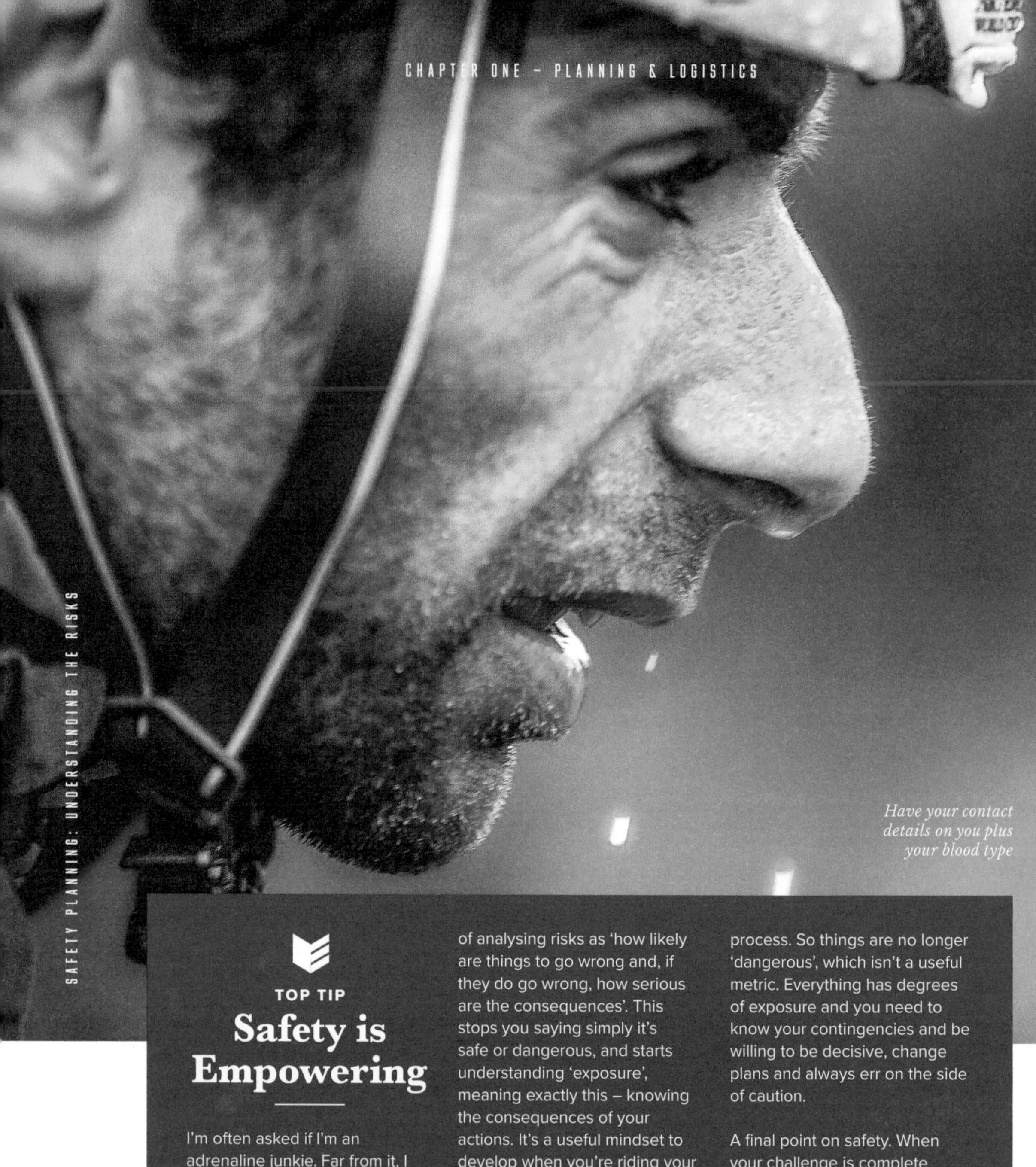

Have your contact details on you plus your blood type

TOP TIP

Safety is Empowering

I'm often asked if I'm an adrenaline junkie. Far from it. I often put myself into situations that others might find hairy, but I've been taking on these expeditions my entire life so have the experience. At the forefront of my mind is riding defensively, which means being road aware, knowing that I'm bottom of the food chain. I describe the process of analysing risks as 'how likely are things to go wrong and, if they do go wrong, how serious are the consequences'. This stops you saying simply it's safe or dangerous, and starts understanding 'exposure', meaning exactly this – knowing the consequences of your actions. It's a useful mindset to develop when you're riding your bike in new areas.

Even being caught out on a long ride when it starts raining and you have forgotten to pack a jacket, what's your exposure? Well, that depends not on how hard it rains, but what the temperature is, which will dictate your decision-making process. So things are no longer 'dangerous', which isn't a useful metric. Everything has degrees of exposure and you need to know your contingencies and be willing to be decisive, change plans and always err on the side of caution.

A final point on safety. When your challenge is complete and you're back riding with mates, remember to use hand signals again, to move around potholes, parked cars, turnings and all the normal courtesies on group rides. It's also easy to get ticked off with vehicles who are discourteous, but never respond in anger. It gets you nowhere and leaves you vulnerable.

"Be aware that travel advice changes quickly, so as much as cyclists' blogs and books can be helpful, ensure your advice is up-to-date"

means how likely it is that something could go wrong and, if it does go wrong, how serious are the consequences. This analysis is more useful than just saying 'it's dangerous'. Here's a real-life example... When I cycled through Ethiopia I considered there to be a high chance of nuisance and low-level crime; I researched many stories of stone throwing and opportunistic crime. I decided that I could deal with this kind of 'risk' myself.

Kenya was less populated and the chances of anything going wrong were lower. However, research showed that many of the recent crimes were far graver. Spillovers from the conflicts in Somalia had led to religious crimes, killings and kidnappings. So even though the chances of such issues were minuscule compared to the nuisance crimes I might experience in Ethiopia, I employed security for a few days, including UK private security and local Kenyan police. Thankfully, I rode through both countries unscathed.

Reasonable risk

On a sliding scale, when I've decided that there's an exposure to risk that I'm not comfortable with, engaging a local tour guide can be sufficient. In other countries, like Pakistan, you're likely to be given protection from the local police – whether you like it or not. They're there to look after you – which is appreciated – but can get in the way of your freedom to explore.

Also be aware that travel advice changes quickly, so as much as cyclists' blogs and books can be helpful, ensure your advice is up-to-date. And drop a courtesy note to your embassy in that country to tell them about your plans, so that if you do need them – even for a lost passport – it isn't the first time they've heard from you.

Have a mentor outside of your close family that you can brainstorm plans before starting any major ride. Even a major single-day ride warrants a 20-minute conversation with someone close (probably your emergency contact) and someone outside of your close bubble. Ideally this contact has experience in this space. This way you can think out loud about nearest hospitals, the equipment you're carrying and your plans if anything was to go wrong.

Always have your name and contact details on you, as well as your blood type and allergies. This can be with a roadID or similar. And have your emergency phone numbers saved in your mobile, as most phones have the ability to bypass your password for someone else to call certain numbers in an emergency.

Chapter One

FINAL THOUGHTS_

A snapshot of how you can achieve your challenging goals...

Logistics is a massive topic, but that doesn't mean that it has to be complicated. That said, for your own sanity and your reputation with cycling buddies, you want to avoid becoming a logistical bore; instead, aim to be dependable, relaxed under pressure with a clear headspace to enjoy the ride.

Broaden Your Horizons

When it comes to routing, I'm a fan of Komoot, where riders can share Highlights and Collections, so that the more people sharing their gravel or road rides, the better the information gets and the easier it is to plan your own.

Less Is More

Get back to the basics with packing, whilst covering the essentials. You'll only live to regret the extra weight on climbs. Pencil in a test ride with your planned gear set-up, seeing how easy it is to load your bike up and strap everything down.

Powerful Networks

For sponsorship, you should build a direct network. Speak to your friends and ask them for introductions. Few people like being asked for sponsorship personally, but we're all proud of who we know, so that's a much easier ask. Your support might come through a second or third point of contact.

Friends 'In The Know'

Friends and family are super important for your support systems, but if they aren't endurance bike riders, they might not 'get it' entirely, so make sure you have friends who understand what you're planning to talk through rationally.

Support Your Support

When it comes to supported rides, you can often rely on friends and volunteers. However, if endurance riding is something you're earning from (you plan to give talks etc), then be careful not to take this goodwill for granted. People who have general skills and want to be along for the adventure are different from professionals (like physios, doctors, coaches) who you are specifically asking to do their job on your ride. Think carefully about how people are thanked, which includes payment if appropriate.

Ride Smartly

In terms of road position, riding defensively does NOT mean cycling along the verge. It means the opposite. Ride well in from the edge, meaning you avoid the worst of the road debris, potholes and tarmac subsidence; you force cars to slow down and pass wider; and you minimise the chance of riding into a car door that opens in front of you.

Aim to be dependable, relaxed under pressure and as calm as possible

Chapter Two

THE MINDSET TO ENDURE

Your endurance exploits will see you ride into psychological depths you never knew existed. Thankfully, you'll soon discover the tools to lift you higher than before

Dreams mean very little without the belief systems to turn them into reality

Chapter Two

THE DOORSTEP MILE

The first step to making your endurance dreams come true is to give your dreams life by telling your friends. You just need to be brave...

MB | **The Scandinavians have a phrase, the 'doorstep mile',** meaning that the first mile away from your front door is the hardest of all. For cyclists, this might mean cycling from home – getting out in the rain and realising it isn't as bad as it looked from indoors. But in a metaphorical sense, the 'doorstep mile' is the ability to take the first step and commit to an event and ride – something you could easily daydream about but never action.

I'm a big fan of dreams, but they mean little without the belief systems and habit of turning them into realities. We're creatures of habit, so therefore committing to ideas and dreams is a habit. People who enjoy lots of adventures have formed a habit of committing to ideas, rather than letting them fizzle away to forgotten wish lists.

The scale of endurance rides can be intimidating but, before any of that, you must commit to the dream. So, here's the trick – be brave for 20 seconds. It's what I tell my children every time they do something new and adventurous – be brave long enough to commit to the task.

For an endurance ride, this is long enough to tell your friend. It's a lot harder to not do something when you've told someone you respect that you'll do it. This is true however long your challenge. Take Jenny Graham. She found it difficult to tell people she'd cycle around the world for the world record. She just wasn't sure she was 'that' person. Saying it out loud to people you trust is an important and empowering step. After that, you get caught up in the excitement of doing, rather than the procrastination of dreaming.

If you want to leave the comfort of your local training loops or your daily commute, then you'll be going outside of your comfort zones to truly test your character: physically, mentally, emotionally, socially and psychologically. You know you're an endurance bike rider when you don't just crave café culture and club rides – you crave freedom.

"I can't believe I'm going to say this as a physiologist, but it's a mindset thing to begin with. You've got to be motivated to do it"

Richard Burden Technical Lead Physiologist at the English Institute of Sport

ENDURANCE STORIES

Climb Like A Grandpa & Summit Like A Kid

The endurance mindset is very different to the racing mindset. Just ask a former professional rider...

GCN presenter James "Hank" Lowsley-Williams explains

I was about to embark on the mountaineering stage of a long-distance cycle and climb with Mark in Ojos del Salado, the world's highest active volcano in Chile, when my guide bestowed that headline upon me, 'Climb like a grandpa and summit like a kid.'

Mark and I had taken a punishing route up the mountain on our bikes, on a journey that'd taken 10 days. Once we got to altitude, the bike and bag of equipment weighed 25kg on our backs. We set up camp at 5,800 metres, ready to walk the remainder of the journey the next day. That night, as we prepared ourselves for the final kilometre of ascent, we were feeling absolutely dreadful. For those who've never been to altitude, it can give you unrelenting headaches that feel like your brain's been clamped in a vice. On top of this, we were dehydrated, sleep deprived and had eaten little. So, we were going into one of the hardest days physically in probably the worst recovery state I'd ever been in.

Coming from a racing background, this was truly mind boggling to get my head around. When I go into a hard race like the Tour of Britain, I've had a week to prepare, to taper, and am physically in the best possible condition. And there I was, on top of a mountain about to attempt the last kilometre of a near-7,000-metre journey with a skull-splitting headache, bike strapped to my back, on about 45 minutes' sleep. Oh, and I nearly forgot to mention – once we'd reach the top, we'd still have to ride 40km →

"We were going into the hardest day physically in the worst recovery state I'd ever been in"

James Lowsley-Williams (right) turned from racer into endurance rider

Smiling – even laughing – in the face of adversity's the best weapon we have

Where will your big ride take you? It took 'Hank' to nearly 7,000 metres... by foot!

ENDURANCE STORIES

"Despite it being our summit day, the end had never felt more illusory or distant"

down the scree slope of a volcano that same day. Sounds great – but extremely intimidating!

Despite it being our summit day, the end had never felt more illusory or distant. I felt every single footstep, each one a conscious labour just to move one foot in front of the next. Our schedule was to break every 20 minutes for a five-minute rest. As soon as we started moving, I was looking forward to the next break.

Edging closer to the goal

My back was aching, my headache was unbearable and my body drained. I crashed down next to my bike, unsure if I could do this anymore. I was mentally and physically spent. I could see the camera lens staring at me and felt close to breaking down in front of it. But as weary as I was, there was something that made me keep going. Well, actually, to be more accurate there were a few things that kept me going – none of them greater than Mark who was somehow still walking ahead. I wasn't going to let him summit alone.

Added to that was the knowledge that I'd spent 10 days on this mountain and I'd suffered too much not to finish it. I dragged myself from the pit I was in, inching my way closer to the top at a painstaking pace. This final hurdle wasn't going to get the better of me. I threw my bike down at the crater just below the peak of the mountain and summoned every last drop of reserve to reach the end.

A dream journey

The emotions are hard to describe. I don't mind admitting that I cried. What a privilege and what a feat of endurance to stand on top of the world's highest volcano. And then, a 300-kilometre ride through the Atacama Desert all the way to the Pacific Ocean – more endurance miles but a dream journey.

When I began my endurance-cycling journey, my mentality was to see it as a race. As soon as I get on a bike, I instinctively want to go full gas and bound off at the front. It took time to realise that I didn't need to go hunting for that effort. Rest assured, it'll find you. It takes discipline to sit back in first gear when you're used to gunning it in fifth and sixth over a four-hour race. You have to think yourself through the battle instead of powering through it. It takes breaking everything down to bite-size chunks and only looking as far as those sections, then moving forward.

In spite of the difficulties, every new endurance challenge I take on →

The beauty of endurance challenges are the unique situations you end up in

ENDURANCE STORIES

“It takes going out and searching for that next big challenge to appreciate what we have”

strengthens me mentally. I can resort back to how I was feeling before and have the confidence to know that I can do it again. It allows me to push the boundaries and go to harder challenges. Once you know that you can handle that much pain, it gets easier to think, ‘You know what? I can handle a bit more.’ Each challenge I take on becomes training for the next one.

Out of the comfort zone

Our day-to-day life can often feel like it doesn’t stretch us enough. For certain people, it takes going out and searching for that effort, that next big challenge, to be able to appreciate the comforts that we have. But the lesson I’ve learnt from endurance sports is that we don’t always need to seize the challenge. Sometimes it takes sitting a little back, like a well-disciplined grandpa in first gear, waiting for the exertion to come to you. And it takes some grit, and a lot of belief, when you get to the top, to finish it with a cheesy grin on your face like the kid who’s just climbed to the top of the world.

‘Hank’, Chilean guide Alvar and Mark celebrate atop the world’s highest volcano

Understanding your psychological arc will set you up to ride further

Chapter Two

ENDURANCE TAKES TIME

Managing your thoughts, focussing on the practical over the emotional, will hold you in good stead whatever your cycling challenge

MB | **You start fresh, dig deep in the middle, and finish exhausted** and elated. Whether you're riding 10 miles, 100 miles or 1,000 miles, we all go through the same psychological arc. 'I left it all out there; I couldn't have done better.' This is human nature. We all justify where we end up in life – it keeps us sane. It applies to an endurance cycle or any other ambition in life.

This highlights a couple of interesting phenomena. Firstly, the power of expectation, meaning no matter how far the journey, we follow the same psychological journey. There's also the power of a plan (which we talked about at length in Chapter 1). Psychological arcs explain why it's hard to do better than what you set out to do. Your legs can already go further than you give them credit for, but your mind has much more fixed ideas. You need to recognise that and unfix before you can extend your comfort zones. You're looking to live longer psychological arcs.

Time is a giant accordion

Endurance athletes develop a trick of being clear on their end goal and never wavering from why it's →

TOP TIP

Mind Over Matter

There are some interesting theories on fatigue, which are worth mentioning without being too exhaustive... Get it! In the 1920's, Archibald Hill introduced a simple theory about the 'central governor', built upon by the work of Tim Noakes in the late 90s. They proposed that the brain regulates exercise so that you can't overexert your body and cause irreversible damage to, for example, the heart muscles. By contrast, there's the idea that fatigue comes from failure of the muscles to maintain their temperature balance.

At the heart of this debate is the question: what is fatigue? Is it a physical or mental construct? I'll let the psychologists and physiologists debate that but, as an athlete, it's worth musing over as fatigue kicks in over those endurance miles. At the low level of output for true ultra-endurance athletes, you shouldn't be breaking down muscle; in theory, you can keep going as long as you keep fuelling. Although, of course, we can't because our minds and body need sleep, need to stop and simply can't suffer indefinite muscle usage. Over ultra-endurance we're more likely to become injured or mentally give up than our muscles fail to function. Ultimately, if you thought cycling was mainly about how strong your legs are, think again!

important. They're focussed on what's in front of them. You can almost always ride the road that you can see – can you then ride to the next horizon and the next? Think about that when you get there, not now.

For sure, there's a part of your mind that's working on logistics down the road, but really focus your mind and make that a practical thought process around fuelling and navigation. Don't let the emotional part of your brain dwell on anything beyond what you can see. It simply wastes

"You can almost always ride the road that you can see – can you then ride to the next horizon or the next?"

precious time and energy. If needed, flit back to visualising why you're doing this in the first place – the purpose. I always imagine time like a giant accordion, which can expand and contract. It doesn't matter if the journey lasts for a morning, a day, a week or half a year, the road will take care of itself if I simply keep going

TOP TIP

Time-Saving Ideas

You may think it's money, but time's the scarcest commodity. Cue these time-saving tips...

Do the important tasks first. We're all good at working through the easy, little jobs, till we run out of time in our day for the big tasks. Running out of time for training is a classic example. But know that you'll be more alert, happier and healthier for having done your fix of exercise, so prioritise it.

Maximise the commute. On foot or by bike gives you such a fitness advantage, because you're doing it every day, rather than playing catch-up at the weekend after a sedentary week. You're training base miles without even thinking of it as training. And once a week, maybe on a Thursday, make a habit of extending your commute; challenge yourself to find new and challenging ways home.

Create a home training set-up. If the commute to the gym or a cycle to work just isn't possible, make sure you have a turbo trainer, rollers or training bike at home. Something on which you can complete a short, high-intensity session whatever's happening in your life.

Recovery is vital. When I lack sleep, my food discipline flies out the window. As the week passes, I must switch off early enough so I can sleep and wake in the right frame of mind. This affects decision making, including my ability to prioritise tasks.

Write notes. You can't beat a hand-written note on the fridge door about food choices or a list before bed to scribble your ideas down for the next day. Switching off from tech an hour before bed helps your recovery, too. In fact, cut down on social-media time full stop. It gives you such poor return on your time investment.

Plan ahead. Taking 1hr on your Sunday to plan your week ahead – what training you're going to do, what snacks you'll prepare, what's your shopping list, what kit needs packing – gives you more mental bandwidth to cope with the week and less opportunity to change your mind, or give you choice when other demands come in or the weather changes!

A mental crash is often a nutritional crash. Food – or lack of it – really affects your mood

and look after myself in the moment – mentally and physically.

Moody? Think food

LP | **Usually, we can tackle the biggest input to our brain power straight** away – our stomach. We are physiological beings. We are what we eat and, when we start to struggle on endurance rides mentally, it normally coincides with an imminent fuelling crisis. When you start to struggle mentally, eat something and drink something. Especially for long rides, this is so, so important.

This is the concept of understanding where your physiology (how your body functions) relates to your psychology (how your head functions). A drop in blood sugar, dehydration, the rising or falling of your core body temperature and sleep fatigue affecting your concentration, these are all physiological changes happening in your body that your brain perceives and interprets with a change in mood, emotion or thought. It's why you might think you're trying to battle mental robustness when eating an energy bar or rice cake might banish those negative thoughts.

So when we talk about mental training, this is the step beyond when you've already ruled out that there isn't a nutritional driver to those thoughts that could be easily changed.

Work through the Prime Cycling Pyramid to boost your chances of goal-getting

Chapter Two

IT'S ALL IN THE MIND

While you might like the idea of 'peak performance', let me introduce you to a more endurance-friendly concept – 'prime performance'

MB | How important is the role of the mind in cycling compared to the physical and technical side? Even a psychologist would struggle to argue that the mind is more important than the body when it comes to endurance cycling, but it's an essential piece of the puzzle. Despite that, it's often neglected. Which is counter-intuitive because we all know it's vital. The inaction arises through lacking a practical framework to maximise the power of the mind.

PRIME CYCLING PYRAMID

Prime Cycling Pyramid
Pain
Emotions
Focus
Intensity
Confidence
Motivation

The PCP gives every cyclist a practical psychological framework

That's where sports psychologist Dr Jim Taylor comes in. 'Prime Cycling' is a phrase that Jim coined in his book *Train the Mind for Athletic Success,* defined as 'riding at a consistently high level under the most challenging conditions'. The detail below's gleaned from online talks and emails that I've had with Jim during the writing of *Endurance.*

Whilst many obsesses over 'peak performance', when it comes to endurance 'peak' is a perilous place as the only way is down! That's why you should aim for 'prime performance', both mentally and physically. Peak might work for Sir Chris Hoy in an Olympics but, for endurance, let's aim for prime. Which brings us to the pyramid to your left...

Motivation

It might be to ride a century or down the coast. It's at the base of the pyramid because motivation is everything.

Confidence

Is a skill that you develop with practice and is defined by how strongly you believe in your ability to achieve your goals. A big part of what you're doing is not just building the physiological abilities to go the distance, but also building a belief in those abilities.

Intensity

We are physical beings. All the mental stuff in the world won't help if →

"We experience pain through a lens of our mind; how we look at pain changes how we experience pain"

you're not physiologically prepared to ride the distance at the speed you want. Intensity is a range from sleep to sheer terror. Somewhere in the middle you'll ride at your best. Your goal is to monitor and adjust your intensity.

Focus

You can't engage in quality training if you're not focussed, especially speedwork. Your body doesn't want to work that hard so, as soon as you let it off the hook, it slows down. Use keywords and, if needed, write them down on your handlebar or top tube. This becomes a mantra and creates focus when times are tough. The 3Ps – positive, process (what do I need to do to ride well) and present (what do I need to do now) – allow you to stay in the moment to focus on what allows you to ride well.

Emotions

Emotions dictate someone's ability to achieve prime cycling. Common emotions in cycling include excitement, joy, pride and inspiration. They also include fear, frustration and despair. Bear in mind that emotions are two sides of the same coin. You can't experience the good ones unless you experience the bad ones. Endurance cycling has an amazing ability to peel the onion away. After a long ride, you're at your purest, for good or bad or ugly. This can be painful but therapeutic and, ultimately, why many of us ride. Ultimately, it makes us feel alive.

Pain

Sensory and emotional experience of discomfort, distress and agony. If it wasn't hard, why do it? A lot of people think pain is a bad thing; in fact, it's essential for us to survive. The thing is, pain no longer protects us from sabre tooth tigers; instead, it simply stops us from pushing ourselves. It's why we have to change our perspective of pain.

There are two parts to pain – physical and psychological. We experience pain through a lens of our mind; how we look at pain changes how we experience pain. The pain when riding is a different sort of pain to a serious injury or illness, which you can't switch off. So whilst cyclists like to talk up a 'sufferfest', it's really not pain – it's physical discomfort because it's not *that* bad. Also, we can switch it off by simply getting off the bike. Mind you, we do need our sense of heroism regardless of how disillusioned that is. So, let's keep using the word pain, but put it into perspective and know what it really is. Accept that it's normal – it means that we're working hard.

The reasons to focus on these words are many: increased motivation; to forge deep and resilient confidence; to settle into a relaxed state of intensity; to train your ability to focus for long periods of time; to create positive emotions and handle negative emotions; and to help you to best master your pain. ⟶

TOP TIP

Smart Goals

The SMARTER framework for goal setting is popular with athletes and stands for Specific, Measurable, Attainable, Realistic, Timely, Evaluate, Reward. The rationale and process is easy to follow and may help you break down the 'What, When, Why and How' of your challenge into more manageable pieces. It's not a framework that I've used personally, simply as I've never found acronyms an easy way of remembering anything. My mind doesn't work that way. But many love them. Give it a try. There are excellent resources online for training using SMART and SMARTER goals.

Retaining focus on the job at hand is vital, especially when it comes to speedwork

Laura's a keen proponent of mindful breathing when stressful situations arise

Chapter Two

COPING MECHANISMS

There are theoretical and applied psychological techniques that'll lift you up when you're feeling low

MB | **This framework by Dr Jim Taylor for how to think about** the mind – Motivation, Confidence, Intensity, Focus, Emotions and Pain – lays the foundations for us to elaborate on coping mechanisms within each section and for Laura and I to weave in our own experiences.

Coping with pain

Let's start at the top of the triangle – Pain. This is normal. It means we're working hard, unless it's an injury, but endurance cyclists become experts at knowing the difference between soreness and injury. The more you train, the more in tune you should become about the changes and the needs of your body. Of course, that soreness or injury isn't binary, and repetitive strain can easily move from manageable discomfort to injury, the distinction being that when you're injured, you shouldn't continue riding. We'll cover this in more detail with bike set-up and endurance conditioning in Chapters 3 and 5. But, for now, let's focus on how we perceive pain.

Thrival means doing well at something and how we perceive this as being worthwhile. To that end, as endurance cyclists, you could accept that pain is a good thing (up to a point), as it tells us we're pushing ourselves and makes us feel 'alive'. Similar to how we deal with all heightened emotions, breathing is one of the key inputs that relax our muscles, which reduces the pain. 'Take a deep breath' might sound obvious and →

Mindful Breathing

LP | Even if you're out of breath, taking deep breaths helps you to regain control of your breathing. Focus on slowing the exhalation part of the breath to claw back control of your breathing. When we're nervous, we have more adrenaline in our system, which increases heart rate and respiratory rate. Slowing your exhalation helps to decrease your heart rate by 'stimulating' the calming part of your nervous system. Imagine when something makes you jump. It's an automatic reaction to inhale quickly and hold our breath. Tension in your body also increases as it's linked with a stimulation of the nervous system. Exhalation however, if slowed, helps to reduce this stimulation. Mindfulness uses breathing as a process of centring, being in the moment and focussing purely on your breath in and out, and feeling the impact it has on your body. This helps to quieten and/or become aware of your thoughts.

over simplistic but read on. Breathing is traditionally thought of as an automatic process, controlled in a similar manner to your heartbeat and sleep patterns. But that's not the full picture. You see, different breathing patterns engage different parts of our brain. This, as Laura explains in the 'Mindful Breathing' box on the previous page, is one way to dampen pain and keep you focussed.

Coping with suffering

I'm often asked how I deal with 'loneliness and boredom' when riding 16 hours a day. Simple. My mind digs up old memories, dreams about the future and explores my imagination.

Endurance riding is wonderfully hard, yet wonderfully simple – you only have one thing to do at any one point in time. We're fickle. I spend half my life on the bike wishing I was at home with all the comforts that brings; when at home, I spend half of my time wishing I was out on the road.

So yes, I've suffered long hours in the saddle, but I've never felt lonely or bored. It's my choice to be there; no-one's forcing me. When the wind's in your face and you're facing your fifth puncture that ride, you might cry. I have and that makes you human. But I often think the only thing worse than going slowly is stopping, so keep those wheels turning. Being accountable means that you have the ability to see the difference between what you can affect and what you can't – and that you have a wry smile in your armoury. Black humour and an →

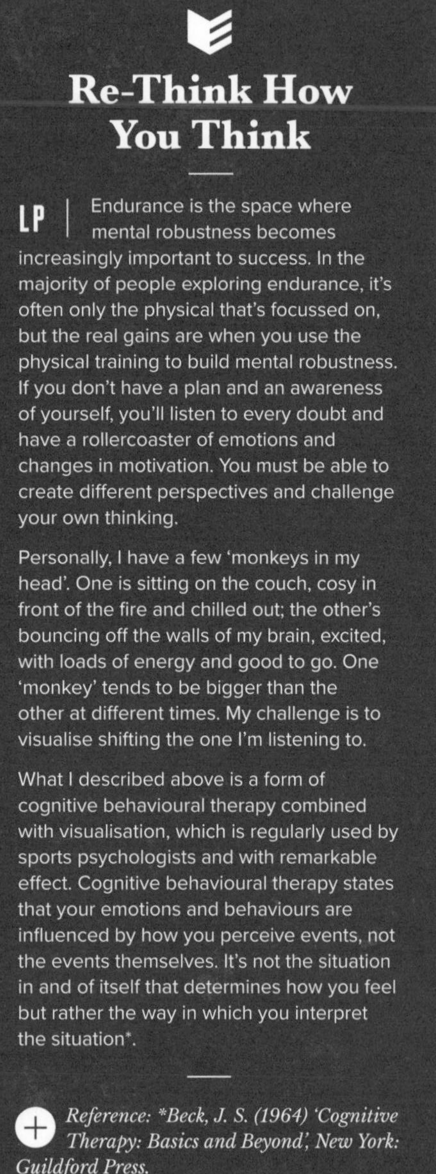

Re-Think How You Think

LP | Endurance is the space where mental robustness becomes increasingly important to success. In the majority of people exploring endurance, it's often only the physical that's focussed on, but the real gains are when you use the physical training to build mental robustness. If you don't have a plan and an awareness of yourself, you'll listen to every doubt and have a rollercoaster of emotions and changes in motivation. You must be able to create different perspectives and challenge your own thinking.

Personally, I have a few 'monkeys in my head'. One is sitting on the couch, cosy in front of the fire and chilled out; the other's bouncing off the walls of my brain, excited, with loads of energy and good to go. One 'monkey' tends to be bigger than the other at different times. My challenge is to visualise shifting the one I'm listening to.

What I described above is a form of cognitive behavioural therapy combined with visualisation, which is regularly used by sports psychologists and with remarkable effect. Cognitive behavioural therapy states that your emotions and behaviours are influenced by how you perceive events, not the events themselves. It's not the situation in and of itself that determines how you feel but rather the way in which you interpret the situation*.

*Reference: *Beck, J. S. (1964) 'Cognitive Therapy: Basics and Beyond', New York: Guildford Press.*

Mental robustness becomes increasingly important the longer you ride

Remember: how you think directs your physical response, not the other way around

"Being accountable means that you have the ability to see the difference between what you can affect and what you can't"

ability to smile through the tears are super-powers – to give a hug of support when it'd be easy to close off the world. If you can maintain objectivity, these moments of great stress and fatigue will become your fondest memories.

Coping with negativity

Fundamentally, stress – whether it's pain, sleep deprivation or not matching your expectations – can close our minds and cloud our judgement. That changes how we communicate with ourselves and others. It also changes our actions. This order is important. Our physical response to a situation is directed by thought processes, not the other way around. And the important link is communication, both self-talk and verbal. In my opinion, behavioural change under pressure is the greatest variable in a person's ability to perform. It's also the biggest factor in how I value my support teams – can people keep an emotional even-keel under pressure? Consistent behaviour (and →

The Power Of Culture

MB | Goals don't just happen, they need to be worked towards and require focussed effort. We also need reference points for our goals. The concept of outliers, in terms of unexplained solo performance, is always embedded in a culture of the right skills and beliefs. I could easily spin the tale that my effort and goals are all mine – the classic self-made, zero-to-hero story of the boyhood dreamer. It's the clichéd narrative for success. Except it's rarely true. We're a result of the cultures we grow up in and the freedoms we've been afforded.

On one side I could say I wasn't a club racer, was never coached, didn't travel until I left school and we weren't financially comfortable growing up, so my goals and efforts have come from nowhere. Or I could tell the full story of how I was home-schooled by a mother who's always supported my desire to explore, and had parents who backed my pedal across Scotland at the age of 12 and drove 1,000 miles in support of my John O'Groats to Land's End at the age of 15. I wasn't coached in a traditional sense, but I was encouraged to follow my ideas. Working on a farm all my life, I also knew what hard, physical work was.

As Dr Jim Taylor explains, if you ask people, especially young cyclists, how many of them have big goals, almost everyone says YES. Then ask how many of you are doing everything you possibly can to achieve your goals, very few people say YES. There's a problem here, which is the disconnect between effort and goals. That leads to two options – you can either lower your goals or raise your effort. There's no right answer – if you don't want to go for the big goals, that's fine. No-one should force you.

If you're aiming for a big goal, you need to have a clear purpose behind why you're doing it in order to stay motivated; if you have big goals that you really want, you have to ask yourself not just once, but regularly throughout the process if you're really doing the work that's necessary.

"When you're hurting the most, focus on why you're doing this because your body's telling you to stop"

performance) under pressure is more valuable in the endurance athlete than the ability to 'smash it' when things are going well.

Generate positive thoughts

People often comment on how 'positive' I must be to jump out of my bed at 3.30am for another 240-mile ride. But I'm no more positive than anyone else. Most importantly, don't give me some 'inspirational quote' when I'm in a dark place. I don't know what to do with that. But I am accountable – I know why it matters to start on time and ride consistently. And I'm not riding 240 miles, I'm simply getting on my bike and riding the first four hours, riding the road in front of me.

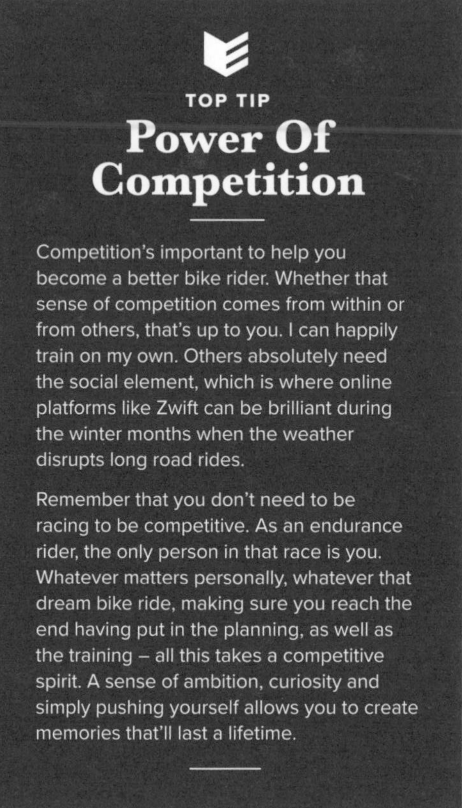

TOP TIP

Power Of Competition

Competition's important to help you become a better bike rider. Whether that sense of competition comes from within or from others, that's up to you. I can happily train on my own. Others absolutely need the social element, which is where online platforms like Zwift can be brilliant during the winter months when the weather disrupts long road rides.

Remember that you don't need to be racing to be competitive. As an endurance rider, the only person in that race is you. Whatever matters personally, whatever that dream bike ride, making sure you reach the end having put in the planning, as well as the training – all this takes a competitive spirit. A sense of ambition, curiosity and simply pushing yourself allows you to create memories that'll last a lifetime.

Coping with 'The Grind'

No matter how much you love to ride, we all get to that point where you're on your bike and it's no longer fun. Most quit or ease up when they reach 'The Grind'. But for cyclists with deeply personal goals, they realise that it's when they hit the grind that it matters. That's what's going to differentiate those who achieve their goals and those that don't.

When you're hurting the most, focus on why you're doing this because your body's communicating that it wants you to stop. And if your mind says, 'Ok, I'll stop' then it's game over. Remember the reason that you're hurting, so this can draw attention away from the pain and produce powerful emotions.

This internal dialogue is powerful; what you say to yourself impacts the way you feel and what you do. If you say to yourself, 'I can't make it up this hill' then you're right. You don't need to say, 'I'm loving this' but you can say, 'I chose to do this.' For many years I've used the mantra 'Time to Commit', which →

Internal dialogue is powerful. It can make or break your ambitions

All of us have deeper reserves of energy and resolve than we think

I've written on my bikes or shortened to TTC. All my ride buddies know what TTC means – and it normally brings out the indignant retorts like, 'I committed a long time ago!' Such self-talk and camaraderie re-focuses and controls negative emotions.

Most of my training is alone. Many endurance cyclists are the same. However, even for the most introverted rider, there's value in sharing training rides and events, at least some of the time. Misery loves company! Plus it doesn't matter how hard you ride when you're alone, you're likely to ride that much harder with someone else there. This can happen virtually as well.

Don't underestimate the power of others to affect motivation. That's why it's so

"It doesn't matter how hard you ride when you're alone, you're likely to ride that much harder with someone else there"

important how you conduct yourself when riding with others. You should also surround yourself with riders who positively influence you. What impact does a ride partner have on you? Do they get more out of yourself and push you? Or do they make you feel despondent? Choose wisely.

Coping with adversity

Remember this: when you think there's nothing left, there's always something left. The human body's adapted →

to always keep something in reserve. But you need to believe there's something left, otherwise you won't act on that reserve. You can understand this through preparation and knowing yourself better – physically and mentally. You're putting money in the 'confidence bank' every time you train, and as there's no overdraft in the endurance world, when it comes to the event you need to have the savings to write that cheque!

It's been proven that smiling, especially when we don't want to, has a physiological and emotional transformation. Tension drains, shoulders drop and you become more relaxed. You aren't going to be happy immediately but it does release endorphins, the body's natural relaxants. It's hard to think and feel down when our body is up. Also, back to emotional leadership, a smile when least expected will either cheer people up or make them think you're tough – either works, so try and force a smile.

As Dr Jim Taylor explains, 'Think about the different physiological responses to situations on the road when you feel anger or despair. Can you ride when you're angry? Yes, for a little while. It might even make you ride faster but not consistently for big miles. Can you ride when you feel true despair? No. Situations create emotional reactions. Whoever loses emotional control first, loses.' Recognise your 'hot button' situations when you become emotionally vulnerable. And have a coping mechanism for when you get there.

Fit & Fits Of Laughter

LP | Confidence goes hand in hand with being physically fit. The fitter I am, the more confident I am, the more confident I am, the more I want to stretch my physical boundaries and greater belief I have in myself in being able to achieve it. This can also mean the reverse – the less fit someone feels, the less confident they are to push themselves, regardless of what they've achieved previously. The negative voice can become the only thing you hear. If you're in a fitness slump, don't look back, only forwards. Focus on the first hurdle of stepping outside the door, then doing something that you enjoy. And then start bringing in short-term goals once you get the endorphins flowing.

And remember that it's better to laugh than cry and, in times of despair, it can be quite amusing what you can find humour in when you're struggling. Laughing at yourself and the situation is much more productive than being despondent.

Maybe yell at yourself (or sing); maybe eat something; maybe change position.

There are four keys to emotional mastery: **1)** Step back and give yourself a bit of distance, gear down; **2)** Let your physiology relax a bit (breathe, change position); **3)** Figure out why you're feeling this emotion (eg I'm frustrated because of a headwind); **4)** Come up with a solution or accept then re-engage.

Smiling through the pain's been scientifically proven to help you dig deeper

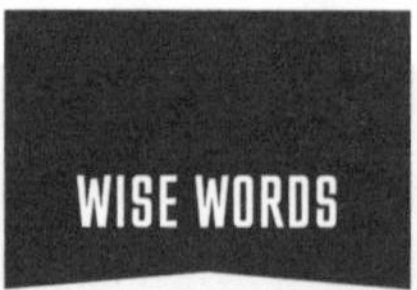

The Confidence To Perform

Techniques like visualisation will strengthen your resolve to reach your goals

ENDURANCE LESSONS WITH
World-renowned sports psychologist Dr Jim Taylor

The words we tell ourselves are critical in determining the path we take to achieve our ambitions. Dr Jim Taylor is a big believer in the power of words. Next are goals – be that winning the Tour de France or finishing a century ride, the victory induces the same psychological reaction. People's goals vary, but the mental obstacles that stand in front of them are universal.

Our insecurities in performance are typically fear based with the most common being fear of failure. To be successful, it's crucial to focus on your own development and not what the people in your social-media feeds are doing.

True achievement takes time

Anybody can go out for a ride when it's flat, the weather's nice and there's a tailwind projecting you forward. The problem is we rarely have these idyllic conditions.

Imagery, or visualisation, is a powerful tool for overcoming obstacles. There's no way to know if you can achieve something until you do it. But you can prepare to complete the event in your mind. There's been a vast amount of research demonstrating that the body and the mind don't know the difference between actual and imagined performance.

A perfect example of the power of imagery is American slalom skier Mikaela Shiffrin. Her first Olympics was 2014. The press asked her, 'What's it like being at your first Olympics?' Her response was, 'It might be my first Olympics from your perspective but, for me, I've been here already. Where? Up here.' She went on to win gold.

To hear more listen to the Endurance podcast on Apple Podcasts, Spotify, Google Podcasts, Amazon Music or search for it on your favourite podcast app.

"People's goals vary, but the mental obstacles that stand in front of them are universal"

Determine your own endurance goals and motivations to be successful

Chapter Two

FINAL THOUGHTS_

Simple but proven techniques to deafen your mind to unproductive noise

Whether it's ensuring you're in the correct gear to climb a stiff mountain, or focussing on the horizon, or just the four-hour block instead of the 240-mile day, keeping in the present can help chip away at the bigger goal. Tapping in to the end goal only occasionally will bring motivation; focus on that big goal too much often demotivates. So just remember that the accordion approach allows you to be adaptable and utilise what focus you need at certain times to get the best out of yourself. And also reflect on other highlights from Chapter 2...

Your Body Affects Your Mind

Understanding the link between physiology and psychology, so you're not putting yourself in a hole when it can simply be solved by fuelling, hydrating properly or accepted more easily if you know you're sleep deprived.

Re-Think How You Think

Cognitive Behavioural Therapy (CBT) is how understanding your thoughts and feelings will influence your behaviour, so how you can recognise those thoughts and feelings early to develop ways to adapt your behaviour.

Use Visualisation

This is a proven and effective tool to create the feelings and sense of purpose of your challenge, while acknowledging the challenges along the way, rather than simply thinking about the finish line.

Take Control Of Your Breathing

Breathing can help quieten the mind, slow the heart rate and regain some control when everything else around you feels like it's taking control of you and you can't change it. The ability to create a mental space when there's no physical space.

Talk To Yourself Like No-One Else Can

Self talk can be really effective when it's specific to you. Think about what phrases may give you that virtual slap in the face to snap you into digging deeper than your mind thinks it can, or calm it down when it's racing.

"Think about what phrases may give you that virtual slap in the face to snap you into digging deeper than your mind thinks it can"

Give yourself regular mindset audits to keep the physical on track

Chapter Three

BODY AND SET-UP

Pedal technique, shoe choice, bike position – all this and more will influence the success of your challenge. Learn how to stay injury-free and ride stronger

A teenage Mark aboard the Peugeot that took him the length of Great Britain

Chapter Two

LOOK BACK TO RIDE STRONG

Before you begin your endurance adventure, it's a motivational boost to reflect on where your love of the bike's come from

MB | **The purpose of this chapter is to build self-awareness for how** you interact with the bike. Watch others, listen to your body, and be willing to tweak your ride and your training to become a smoother rider. When it comes to endurance, efficiency rules.

But before we're lost in the geekery of biomechanics and anatomy, a rose-tinted look back at my bikes and what brought me to caring about how well they fit. My first bike was a white Peugeot 15-speed, which I completed my first road adventure on – a mighty 18 miles at the age of 10. Before, I'd ridden hand-me-downs from my big sister, Heather. At 12 I cycled across Scotland on the road... upon a mountain bike with knobbly tyres!

I then became obsessed with the Tour de France and Mario Cippollini. So the dream was set on a CAAD3 aluminium, red Cannondale. At 15 I bought a second-hand road bike – another Peugeot – that took me over 1,000 miles from John O'Groats to Land's End.

This ignited my roadie passion. For the next few years, I saved lunch money and took on a part-time job to save for a better bike. For reasons forgotten, I opted for a Specialized Allez Comp over the Cannondale, which was loved and used, but I sold it at uni to fund a summer holiday travelling across Canada – a decision I'd later regret when I returned and started dreaming of cycling around the world, only to realise I was left with a mountain bike! By the time I trained to cycle around the world – the first time – I could only afford a second-hand Fausto Coppi. It was too small for me, but I still rode thousands of miles on it.

Europe on an MTB

I then cycled the length of Europe on an entry-level Specialized Rockhopper mountain bike, converted for road riding via rigid forks and slick tyres. However, it was too small for me and left me with chronic tendonitis. Still, I have fond memories of that bike and still have it. But it told me that size matters!

I share all of this in part so you can reflect on your formative years on two wheels and remember where the passion started. I didn't grow up with bike fitters, coaches, club rides and races – I grew up having adventures, without a care, albeit on badly fitting bikes. However, you can avoid my many years of mistakes by caring more than I did when I started out about biomechanics and sports science!

Efficient pedalling is vital over long distances. Aim to reduce the 'flat spots'

Chapter Three

PEDAL POWER_

Like any skill, working on your pedalling technique will maximise each and every ounce of effort, while reducing the chances of injury

LP | **Here's a brief biology lesson on pedalling: the gluteus maximus** (backside), quadriceps (front of upper leg) and hamstrings (back of upper leg) do most of the work when riding a bicycle, supported by the gastrocnemius, soleus and tibialis anterior in the calf and front of shin. These muscles work together to generate the pedalling action. Muscles such as the adductors (inside your thigh) and muscles deep around the hips work to counteract sideways movement and support a linear drive through the crank. Finally, you have the muscles in your back, neck and trunk, all working isometrically (contract without the body part moving) to sustain your position. On longer rides, it's often the neck and back where you feel fatigue really setting in.

MB | The most common descriptor of the pedal stroke is the face of a clock, where 12 is the top of the pedal stroke and six is the bottom. One of the reasons that cleats are recommended is to maximise the second half of the pedal stroke. Another reason is so the →

Pedal Muscles

The drive of the power phase is initiated by the glutes when starting from 12 to three o'clock. The knee extensors/quads then overlap and take dominance in the three to six o'clock range. As your leg comes towards the bottom of the crank angle from five to six o'clock, the plantar flexors/calf muscle group is dominant. This shifts to the anterior shin as you begin the pull phase. From seven to nine o'clock the hamstrings/knee flexors start supporting the anterior shin in pulling the knee through flexion and then, finally, the hip flexors kick in from nine to 12 o'clock to pull the hip up in to hip flexion.

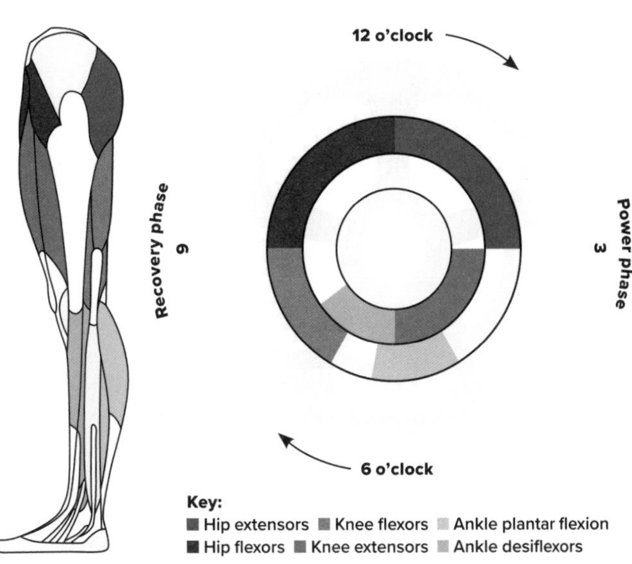

pedal sits beneath the ball of the foot. You can then use your ankle as a power lever.

If you've ever sat on a trainer bike that shows pedal efficiency, it might look like an inefficient figure-of-eight compared to a smoother-pedalling peanut shape. If you stomp, meaning all your power is between 12 and six o'clock, you have 'flat spots' of power precisely at 12 and six, where the momentum of the pedal stroke takes you through to the next 'stomp'. Try pushing the toe across the 12 and 'scraping' it back through the six for more efficient pedalling, though over very long distances, don't exaggerate this movement or you could strain your Achilles tendon.

Invest in your sole

Cycling shoes optimise power transfer compared to trainers or soft-sole shoes. I'd also recommend custom insoles. Most people focus on their backside, but I'd argue that your feet are the most important and often forgotten contact point with your bike. If your foot's not supported properly inside the shoe, the issues are transferred up the leg, most likely with the knee folding inwards during the downstroke. Look down at your legs as you pedal at a normal cadence (80-100rpm) – do your knees move up and down like pistons or do they drop in towards the top tube? Now shift through the gears till your cadence is 60-70rpm. As you're working harder, has this changed the symmetry of your knees? These observations tell you whether your foot needs better support before you experience a knee twinge.

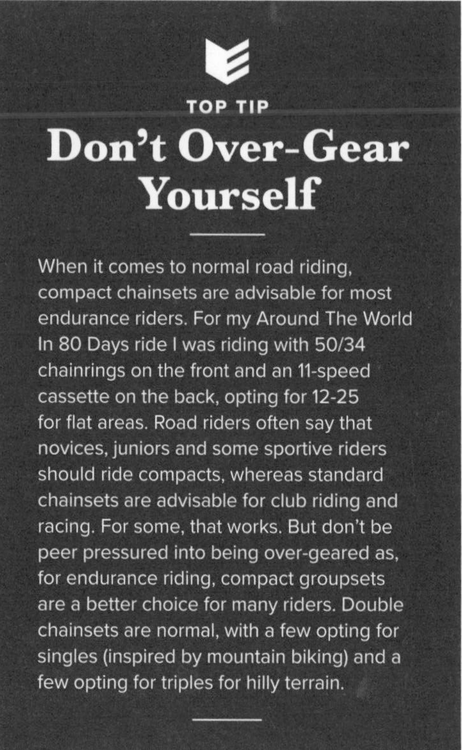

TOP TIP

Don't Over-Gear Yourself

When it comes to normal road riding, compact chainsets are advisable for most endurance riders. For my Around The World In 80 Days ride I was riding with 50/34 chainrings on the front and an 11-speed cassette on the back, opting for 12-25 for flat areas. Road riders often say that novices, juniors and some sportive riders should ride compacts, whereas standard chainsets are advisable for club riding and racing. For some, that works. But don't be peer pressured into being over-geared as, for endurance riding, compact groupsets are a better choice for many riders. Double chainsets are normal, with a few opting for singles (inspired by mountain biking) and a few opting for triples for hilly terrain.

Saddle and bar set-up

When the pedal sits at six o'clock, there should be about 25 degrees of knee bend. This is a quick check if you think your saddle's slipped or you've jumped on a hire bike, but here's a more accurate method. Measure your inseam (crotch to floor) then multiply this number by 0.883 to give you a decent saddle-height guide from the centre of your bottom bracket. However, if you ride non-standard cranks (more or less than 175mm) then this won't be accurate; instead, take this inseam number and multiply by 1.09, then use this figure from the top →

Position your cleats further back towards the heel of the shoe for endurance riding

Read the terrain, pre-empt changes in rolling resistance and maintain a cadence of 80-100rpm

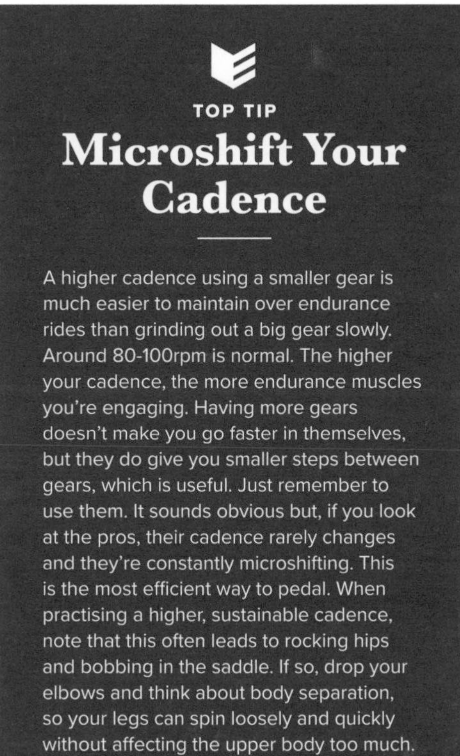

TOP TIP

Microshift Your Cadence

A higher cadence using a smaller gear is much easier to maintain over endurance rides than grinding out a big gear slowly. Around 80-100rpm is normal. The higher your cadence, the more endurance muscles you're engaging. Having more gears doesn't make you go faster in themselves, but they do give you smaller steps between gears, which is useful. Just remember to use them. It sounds obvious but, if you look at the pros, their cadence rarely changes and they're constantly microshifting. This is the most efficient way to pedal. When practising a higher, sustainable cadence, note that this often leads to rocking hips and bobbing in the saddle. If so, drop your elbows and think about body separation, so your legs can spin loosely and quickly without affecting the upper body too much.

of the pedal sitting at six o'clock to the top of your saddle. To check this, clamp your bike into an indoor trainer or ask someone to hold the bars, then pedal backwards with your heels on the pedals. Your hips should be steady – no rocking forwards and back. Drop the saddle till the rocking stops.

When seeking your perfect fit, start with your saddle flat and positioned halfway along the rails. Saddle position affects pedal fluidity more than handlebar set-up, so if you need more reach I'd try a longer stem before pushing your saddle back, as the aft position causes you to reach at the front of the pedal stroke and overextend your knee. The theoretical ideal is drawing an imaginary line straight down from your knee when it sits at three o'clock. The line should cut through the ball of your foot, the cleat and, therefore, the axle of the pedal.

"Saddle position affects pedal fluidity more than handlebar set-up"

Proficient cockpit fit

You need greater reach on an endurance bike than a normal road set-up, so the angles, especially for your neck, aren't as severe. This might mean going up a frame size or fitting a longer stem. You also normally need extra height (spacers) on your headset. Fitting tri-bars is a great idea for solo riding, giving you plenty of space to stretch out. When fitting tri-bars, put spacers underneath so you still have room to hold the flats of your bars.

If bike packing with a bar bag, your cockpit will be squeezed for space. That's why wide-enough handlebars are essential and of a shape that allows at least three separate hand positions (not counting the tri-bar position). Double taping your bars with either 2.5mm or thicker, especially around the top of the bars from the flats to the hoods, dampens road buzz and so reduces the potential of nerve damage on long rides.

Chapter Three

CLEAT OF CHOICE

Your connection with your bike's arguably the most important relationship you'll have on two wheels. Cue cleat selection

MB | **When endurance road riding and unsupported, you're likely** to want the flexibility of mountain-bike or gravel shoes, so you can get off and walk. And unlike road versions, you can also clip in and out on both sides of the pedal. For supported endurance road rides, road cleats are preferred, as they provide greater surface area for your power to transfer through. Riding the length of Africa using SPDs (type of cleat; small) left me with sores under the cleats, but then again different insoles might have alleviated this.

Cleat position

All cleats have a range of positions where they can sit on the sole. This determines the comfort of your feet, ankles, knees, hips and back. If you're riding road cleats, these usually have less float (lateral movement) so choose a model that has as much as possible. Keep in mind that for SPDs and many others, the float's built into the pedal and not the cleat. Place cleats further back for endurance riding, so reducing ankle leverage.

Cleats usually run straight down the midline of the shoe, but we're all different so start from this neutral position and make changes if needed. Just be aware that if cleats sit too near the bottom bracket (on the inside of the shoe), this can cause the toes to point in and lead to extra strain on the outside of the leg (iliotibial band). Conversely, inside (medial) knee strain normally stems from an external rotation (toes outwards). A narrower stance is better for efficient pedalling but, if you have big feet, that might not be feasible as you'll rub the crank. In all cases, the cleats should be positioned so that the ball of your foot's over the pedal axle. Remember to make small changes at a time as millimetres in the foot are multiplied many times over by the time you reach the knee and hip.

Cleat wedges

Most of us pronate (rotate down through the midfoot), but some have a rigid or raised midfoot that means they stay in supination (lifted through the midfoot). This can influence knee angle either inwards or outwards. Get an orthotic first, and then consider wedges beneath the cleats to help neutralise the problem. If you have a good fit inside your shoe, looking down at your knee angle on the pedal rotation should tell you whether you need to slightly wedge the cleat to get it flat. Cycling shoes, cleats and pedals force your natural tilt flat, which needs to be compensated somewhere, normally in the knees. The difference this can make in terms of pressure through your knee and good alignment through the hips on endurance rides is massive.

Wider road cleats (left) are preferable to SPD-style cleats on supported endurance rides

TOP TIP

Gear Up, Get Up!

When you rise out of the saddle, shift up two gears beforehand so you have more resistance to counter your bodyweight on the pedals. This kind of pre-emptive gear changing's also important when riding with others, dropping on their wheel or holding pace lines, so that there's no jump in your pace and so avoids touching of wheels. This also explains why you should remain seated when ascending in groups. It's difficult for even experienced riders to suddenly lift out of the saddle without abruptly slowing down, causing the rider behind to reach for the brakes at a time when they need all their momentum to ride uphill.

When climbing out of the saddle, shift up a couple gears for greater resistance

Chapter Three

BODY SEPARATION

A serene swan up top and fast, fluid legs below equals efficient energy output and sustainable power

MB | **Body separation is where the upper body stays neutral (still)** while the legs spin fluidly beneath. Too low a saddle and muscle fatigue are common causes to upset this harmony, so ask your ride buddies to comment on your form during long rides and change things if necessary. You want to keep your upper body as relaxed as possible – wasted movement leaches energy – even when climbing out of the saddle.

When climbing, drop down through the gears and spin a higher cadence than normal. Be aware of your core, and drop your elbows and shoulders so your upper body's as relaxed as possible, pushing your bum back in the saddle and moving your hands to the flats of the bars. Only lift out of the saddle if you need to release pressure in your back or legs, or if it becomes too steep. Into the wind, again stay seated if you can to preserve energy – a precious resource on long rides.

Gripping bars too hard is another energy waster, but common when fatigued. It locks out your upper body, which impairs pedal fluidity. It's also uncomfortable, as you stop soaking up bumps in the road via the suspension of your arms. Again, the input to remedy this is your elbows. You can't be A-framed or white knuckled if your elbows drop, staying as parallel to the road as possible. When hands tighten, arms tighten, shoulders hunch, centre of gravity comes up, power goes down, you slow down. So shake out fingers and arms, focus on where your elbows are, and your upper body will stay nice and neutral, so you can keep your cadence high.

When I was a boy, learning to ride a pony, I was told to hold the reins like I was holding a chick – squeeze too hard and you kill it! Same for cycling – you want to be relaxed on the bars, while maintaining control. Putting your weight through the crook of your thumb on the hoods of the brakes will end up hurting over long miles. Slide the hands back a little when possible. Holding the hoods is needed for technical descents or in traffic but, when climbing, place your fingers on the flats of the bars, closer to the stem, sitting further back in the saddle, which engages the glutes fully, stabilises your upper body and delivers an efficient climb.

"Only lift out of the saddle if you need to release pressure win your back or legs, or if it becomes too steep"

ENDURANCE STORIES

Cause, Not Effect

Mark's suffered more than most, but key to endurance progression is to identify the cause of any issues, not the symptoms

ENDURANCE STORIES with Mark Beaumont

During the Around Britain 3,000-mile training ride before the 80 Days, the hope was that I'd spend most of each day in the tri-bars, leaning forward, aerodynamic and putting less weight directly onto the saddle. But with the constant hills on the west coast I'd been sitting upright almost all the time, hands on the brake hoods. This wasn't helping my hands or neck. Many of the nerves in your hands meet in the fleshy pad at the base of your little finger. The ulnar nerve then weaves its way up the length of the arm, into the shoulder, meaning my hand numbing and neck pain were directly related.

Laura and my team were worried about this, wanting to see me in a more efficient position, concerned that I couldn't hold the time-trial position for long hours. I was still confident the issue was the terrain, as opposed to my bike fit or flexibility. But a further consequence of how I'd been riding – upright – was that my backside was painful. And the catalyst for taking this from a bearable pain to unadulterated rawness was the constant rain.

'Remove your shorts, now!'

While camped at John O'Groats, someone suggested I pull on a second pair of bib shorts as an extra layer of padding. The result? Simply wonderful. I pedalled southwards far happier, enjoying the flatter roads of the east coast and so being able to find the time-trial position more often. Double shorts seemed like a great solution. But it turned out to be a serious mistake.

My right leg grew more painful and weaker over the next four days. It didn't bode well for the world cycle that was only a few months away. That's when Laura ordered me to remove my second pair of shorts! I was so saddle sore and in such a depleted state, it hadn't occurred to me. It transpired that →

"The catalyst for taking this from bearable pain to unadulterated rawness was the constant rain"

Understanding the cause of pain should lead to prevention down the line

Cycling stresses most parts of your being, so monitor yourself from head to toe

"Build the awareness to stop and think – what's changed that's caused this issue in my body?"

the double elastic and tension around my thighs was the issue. The repeated rubbing over 16 hours beneath shorts that were too tight had caused a small tear in my hamstring muscle. It seems obvious but sleep deprivation had clouded my thinking.

Be your own auditor

The wider lesson learnt over the coming days wasn't so much about clothing, it was about spotting more quickly when things go wrong. Any little niggles, any changes in form, needed to be noted and analysed before they became a big problem. This applied to all of us. The team needed to maintain the ability to step away from the coalface and constantly ask questions: 'Why has that happened?', 'What's changed?' Tiny issues can escalate quickly, whether that's dynamics within the team or something practical with the athlete or the bike. We had to be able to self-monitor and keep tweaking the plan. Far easier said than done when you're caught up in the challenge. Looking back on Around Britain we 'only' averaged 225 miles a day. I was mentally battered by how tough this training ride had been. I was just focussed on the next hour, not thinking too far ahead, worried about the pain and gradually slowing down.

From there I had nine weeks to recover for the start of the 240-mile-a-day circumnavigation – not ideal with a tear in the hamstring. But it taught me a lesson about self-monitoring. This set me up for the 18,000-mile race, so that when I subsequently felt a slight twinge in my knee, we didn't treat my knee pain, but instead immediately changed my cleats, knowing that an input had changed, which had caused a repetitive strain, rather than thinking my knee had suddenly become injured by itself. Obvious? Maybe, but not when you're on the bike, so build the awareness to stop and think – what's changed that's caused this issue in my body?

Chapter Three

COMMON INJURIES AND HOW BEST TO AVOID THEM

Endurance cycling's potentially derailed by a number of set-up issues. But not if you read on…

MB | **Pain is your body's way of letting you know you're causing** damage. At the same time, breaking down some muscle and allowing enough recovery is essential to grow stronger. During the training phase, you need to build tolerance to this level of discomfort to allow the body's natural adaptation to endurance.

"You learn the difference between being sore and injured over big miles"

Being aware of your body through endurance is different to being aware of your body through short events. You must spot the difference between being sore and being injured. With experience, you understand what you can ride through and when it's wise to stop. Conditioning is something you can only improve and build tolerance through by pushing through, whereas repetitive strains are only going to get worse with more miles.

When it comes to repetitive-strain injuries, knee and hip pain are the most common and normally arise from doing too much too fast. This might be early season training or at the start of an expedition ride. Time off the bike helps but, in terms of active adaptation, your best option is to gear back, spin a higher cadence and avoid hill work. Pushing big gears, especially in cold weather, will aggravate knee and hip issues.

In terms of set-up, you may be riding with a saddle that's the wrong height – likely too low – cleats that aren't aligned perfectly or have the incorrect crank length. Standard cranks are 175mm, but we riders aren't all 'standard sizes', so for particularly tall or short riders, or injured riders, try other crank lengths. For hips with impingement issues, for instance, a shorter crank will give you greater clearance at the top of your pedal stroke.

You can also trial pedal spacers, which take the pedal away from the crank arm, normally by 20mm – helpful for cyclists who are having issues with knees out. Spacers can also be useful for people with extra-wide feet, wide hips or if you're experiencing discomfort on the outside of your knee. That's an overview of the problems you can →

Pushing big gears, especially in the cold, can aggravate knee issues

Small changes make a big difference to pedalling fluidity and injury prevention

encounter when cranking up the mileage. Now, read on to focus on specific issues plus, thankfully, ways to prevent them in the first place...

Knee pain

Knee pain tends to develop over long days. During big rides, rest often isn't possible, so tweaking your position on the bike, as well as rest, ice and elevation when off the bike, are important. If you can't rest entirely, reduce your riding by 25% and spin a higher cadence. But as prevention's the best cure, check biomechanics at a bike fitter, learn to increase your cadence if you're someone that pushes high gears, avoid big jumps in riding intensities or mileages, and cover your legs in cold weather.

Runner's knee

Related to these issues is 'runner's knee' or 'chondromalacia', where the cartilage on the underside of the kneecap (patella) deteriorates. This is more common in female cyclists, possibly due to a wider pelvic angle increasing the quads angle and adding a compressive element to the patella. The main solutions are reviewing your biomechanics before jumping to treatment. Shortening your crank length can decrease the load on your kneecap at the front of the pedal stroke. Again, learning to ride a higher cadence helps. In terms of your pedal stroke, there should be no lateral motion, so watch your knees. It's possible to retrain muscle memory in your pedal stroke. Off the bike, strengthening the external rotators of your hip, the inside of your calf (medial gastrocnemius) and the inside of your quads (the VMO) will help to stabilise the entire knee. Also, foam roller the outside of your quads and lateral calf. Most beginner cyclists ride with the saddle a bit low and this hurts the knees over big miles – a small adjustment upwards can make a big difference.

Tendon problems

LP | Sudden jumps in ride load can lead to tendinopathy (changes in the tendon tissue) or causes the outer sheath (para-tendon) surrounding the tendon to become inflamed (para-tendonitis). If you continue to cycle with Achilles para-tendonitis, it can cause further inflammation, resulting in fluid build-up between the tendon and the outer sheath. This feels like a rusty hinge. If particularly bad, it can sound like squeaky polystyrene. This is called 'crepitus' and it hurts.

Firstly, you'll need an accurate diagnosis by a physio or sports doctor. Achilles or patella tendon pain is similar, whether it's para-tendonitis, tendinopathy or a small tendon tear. However, each is treated differently. Para-tendonitis →

"Most beginner cyclists ride with the saddle a bit low and this hurts the knees over big miles – a small adjustment upwards can make a big difference"

requires ice, topical anti-inflammatories and, in the initial stages, a reduction in training load; tendinopathy actually requires heavy loading put through it in a controlled and dosed way; a tendon tear requires offloading initially and then loading in a shortened position, which is why it's vital to get an accurate diagnosis.

MB | My 1,300-mile ride through Scandinavia, on a mountain bike that was too small for me, left me with tendonitis in my knees and ankles. This trip was a lesson in properly fitting your bike and biomechanics. Even leaving Paris at the start of the 80 Days, I experienced minor para-tendonitis in my knees and was concerned it'd be with me over the coming months. Thankfully, small changes to my cleat wedges, keeping cadence high and not pushing too hard in the first week settled things down.

Pain in the feet

I've had many foot issues and they always feel like I'm riding on hot coals, which isn't great as you can't effectively transfer power. You also compensate by shifting weight and tilting your feet, leading to ankle, knee and hip issues as the misalignment's transferred up your legs.

A raised foot arch collapses under power, so ensure your foot's nice and stable in your shoe. Any movement should come from the cleats, not your foot. If your foot does move, problems occur up the kinetic chain. Your lower leg rotates, as does your knee and then hip. It's a recipe for disaster. Soft-soled shoes can also be a problem. Ride a century in a pair and you'll likely feel plantar-fascia aggravation because of a degree of foot movement upon the cushioned sole.

Full carbon race soles, however, can be so stiff that over long rides they give you hot spots or pins and needles beneath the cleats. Yes, you need the rigidity of the shoe's foot plate but also the right level of cushioning to support the natural contour of your foot at rest.

"Para-tendonitis requires ice, topical anti-inflammatories and a reduction in training load"

You also need to be aware of too tight a toe box, which can result in excruciating cramps. Many of us suffer from sore feet on long rides. How do you react? Often by involuntarily scrunching the toes and pointing them downwards. It might ease things temporarily. The problem is this can irritate the Achilles tendon sheath (the tendon running down the back of the heel attaching to the lower calf), again driving up the leg and resulting in further knee or hip pain.

Numbness is common, too, and caused by compression of the nerves that sit between the small bones beneath the ball of the foot – the metatarsals. Tight shoes, road buzz, high arches and too much power work when lacking →

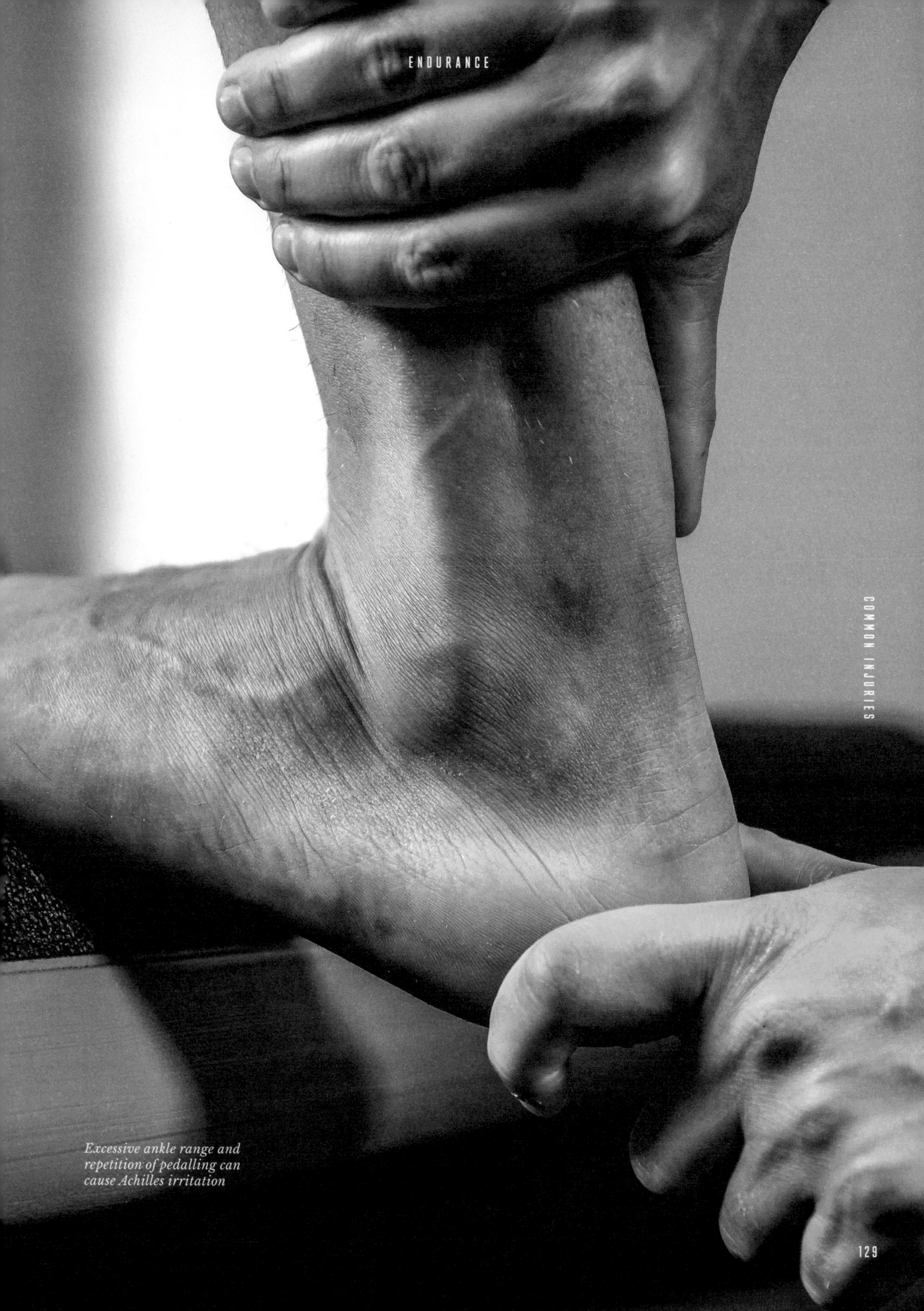

Excessive ankle range and repetition of pedalling can cause Achilles irritation

conditioning are all guilty parties. Quick fixes include: moving the cleats backwards; loosening shoe closures; changing insoles (thinner if shoe is too tight) or using custom footbeds; a different sock (for the same reasons); feel

"Long climbs can cause back pain because the muscles work harder during seated climbs as they're supporting the upper body"

around the inside of your shoe for seams, laces or buckles that are causing pressure; or simply find a wider shoe.

Back pain

Long climbs can cause back pain because the muscles work harder during seated climbs as they're supporting the upper body. It's one reason why core training's so important for cyclists. As is your bike set-up. While not essential – I didn't have one until I was 33 years old and had cycled to about 100 countries by that point – a pro bike fit takes the guesswork out of perfect positioning. Just note that what felt right on the bike-fitting rig might feel too high during a long ride. Rocking in the seated position and reaching out at the bottom of the pedal stroke are both signs of too high a saddle. Drop it and it'll ease lower-back tension.

That said, more people ride with their saddle too low than too high, which raises the spectre of tendinopathy in the knees and ankles. Numbing of the undercarriage could be caused by the same issue or it could be that your saddle is slightly nose-up.

Power to your pedals – these vital and unexplored contact points transport your riding

Hand and neck injuries

Shermer's Neck is a condition where the neck muscles fail from fatigue and can no longer support the head. It's named after Michael Shermer, one of the first Race Across America competitors, who lost the ability to hold his neck up and had to prop his head up with his hands to carry on. It's a rare ailment simply because most will never be on a bike for the 500-plus-mile minimum it takes for Shermer's Neck to pop up.

LP | Shermer's Neck is an extreme condition and, thankfully, rarely seen outside of ultra-endurance events. Neck pain, however, is common for a rider who's significantly upping ride length, especially over multiple days. Conditioning your neck muscles and upper back to act against gravity (we'll discuss this in more detail later) or having a good bike set-up both help.

If you're experiencing recurrent headaches during rides and know you're hydrated, have your neck position looked at because it could be compression at the top of the neck/base of your head. If you have an underlying neck issue, such as a grumbling disc or overloaded joint, it can lead to compression or irritation of the nerve at the root or where it exits from the spine. This can manifest itself as constant pain in the shoulder blade or pins and needles down the arm or in the hands. It can even lead to reduced grip strength, which lingers even when off the bike. If you're showing these symptoms, seek out a sports doctor and/or physio.

We're all unique. It's why saddle choice is very much an individual thing

Chapter Three

SADDLE HEALTH

Finding the saddle for you will lay the perfect platform for success, resulting in more comfort and better riding

LP | **Saddle issues can lead to bruising of the pubic bones, saddle sores,** vulva issues for women (which is why many give up cycling) or, for men, potentially erectile dysfunction or impotence. This is due to compression on the pudendal and perineal nerves. None of this should be accepted as the norm. Make changes until you can ride without numbness or saddle issues.

Nerve entrapment

Nerves are on a two-way street. One type of nerve travels from the periphery, whether that's sensors in the skin, joints, tendons or muscles. Signals are sent via sensory nerves to the spinal cord and then to the brain, where they're perceived and acted on. A connection from the brain to the muscles asks the muscle to contract (motor nerves).

"If there's entrapment of the pudendal nerve, you can experience pins and needles"

Nerves like to move but don't have as much extensibility as muscles and tendons. When we move, they glide and slide but don't stretch too well and can often be caught or compressed in narrow spaces. A classic example is when you awake in the night with a 'dead arm' due to falling asleep with an arm in the closed position. The nerve's compressed for a long time because of lying on it, resulting in numbness. However, once you take the weight off your arm, open out your elbow and move your shoulder, the nerve's free again, the signals reflow, bloodflow returns and those symptoms subside.

Apply this principle to the nerves that emanate from your spinal cord and under your tailbone, passing beneath your pelvis and into your perineum. Sitting on this area for hours, so that the nerve's compressed or the surrounding muscles are stretching and compressing the nerve that way, you can see how the nerve's agitated, leading to pain.

The pudendal nerve's present in both male and female, and is the motor supply to many of the pelvic muscles as well as those that control urination or final bowel transmission. It also provides the sensory nerve supply to the external genitalia. In turn, if there's entrapment or compression of the pudendal nerve, you can experience pins and needles, numbness or pain in those areas. In extreme cases, it's mooted that the rider can suffer from erectile dysfunction, albeit evidence of this isn't →

conclusive. If you're experiencing any of these symptoms, seek medical advice.

Tips for sitting pretty

So how can you sit more comfortably? Well, these tips are a good place to start...

— **Get your bike fit right**
If your saddle's too high or too low, if you're over reaching to reach the hoods, if your saddle's angled too much in one direction, all of these can add up to increased movement across the saddle. This creates friction and greater compression on areas of your pubic bones and other areas underneath.

— **Choose your saddle wisely**
You might want a padded saddle but don't make it too wide and squishy as the more suitable saddle's often narrower and harder. Measuring the width of your sit bones is important but, once rotated forwards, your weight isn't only on these bones, so avoid a wide saddle. It's worth considering a nose-less saddle or one with a central groove to ensure there's no entrapment of either the pudendal or perineal nerves.

— **Try saddle mapping**
Some bike fitters and retailers offer this service, giving you real-time saddle-pressure visualisation as you pedal. At GB Cycling, this was taken to the extreme when they created a cast of the cyclist's under-carriage to ensure that their saddles were designed for the rider.

— **Improve your trunk strength**
Imagine you're trying to drill a hole in the wall but you're standing on a Swiss ball. You just can't put power through the drill in a direct path. Now think how easy it'd be if you were wearing lead boots and standing on a solid surface. Applying this analogy to the bike, your legs are the drill. They're connected to your pelvis and your trunk – aka your foundation. If your trunk's like a wobbly Swiss ball with no muscular stiffness, the drive through your legs is diluted. In short, strengthening your core creates a stable base from which to generate more force.

— **Don't wear underwear**
Wearing pants under your bib shorts can create extra friction and discomfort.

— **Use chamois cream**
Chamois cream and Sudocrem are effective for preventing saddle sores.

— **Trim pubic hair**
This goes for both women and men. Short pubic hair allows for better sweat and heat transfer, creating areas of micro airflow. Don't go too far, though. With shaving there's a high risk of in-growing hair and subsequent infection. Waxing or laser treatment leaves little in the way of preventing friction on the fragile skin.

— **Prioritise hygiene**
Washing with clean water and not using soaps that strip away the natural antibacterial environment, making sure you're dry afterwards and then applying a thin layer of antibacterial moisturising cream, really help to recover post rides.

No pants and chamois cream will reduce friction and improve comfort

Chapter Three

STRENGTH & CONDITIONING

An increasing amount of research stresses the importance of off-the-bike work on endurance rides

LP | **There's no amount of gym work that can adapt your body as** effectively as time in the saddle. However, upping your ability to withstand constant repetitive load will not only reduce risk of overuse injuries, but will also make you more energy efficient on the bike.

Understanding what you're training for is important to build better conditioning. It could be a long, flat ride for hours, which raises awareness of lower-back and neck endurance; a six-hour ride in the hills that focusses the spotlight on your knees or Achilles; a five-hour ride with a strong crosswind where you challenge your trunk strength. This knowledge, plus an understanding of previous injuries and limitations, helps you to shape your 'off-bike' plan. A review with a sports physio will help, too. They'll assess restrictions in range at your hips, for example, and then prescribe a programme if needed.

Strong core, longer rides

As cyclists we tend to rest on our hands, on the hoods, with outstretched arms while our bums are resting on the saddle carrying much of our weight. This creates what's called 'tripod splinting', meaning we rely on resting on our passive skeleton and, in the process, seemingly ask little of our muscular system or, in this case, the trunk. This is a mistake. See Chapter Five, p192, for specific off-the-bike circuits.

Neck & Back Conditioning

LP | During a long ride, your lower back will predominantly be in flexion, meaning the tissues (muscle/tendons/ligaments) around the spinal joints would have been at length for that duration. Leaving tissues on stretch for a long period means they endure a 'creep' response, so they start to elongate and lose some stiffness, elasticity and contractile ability.

At your neck the opposite happens – you spend your time in extension, so the tissues on the back of your neck are in constant compression at the joints or contraction in the muscle tissue, which can lead to muscle fatigue. That's why it's important to condition these two areas off the bike, to build the capacity of the muscles to withstand the endurance and also to build support in surrounding muscles to provide some offload.

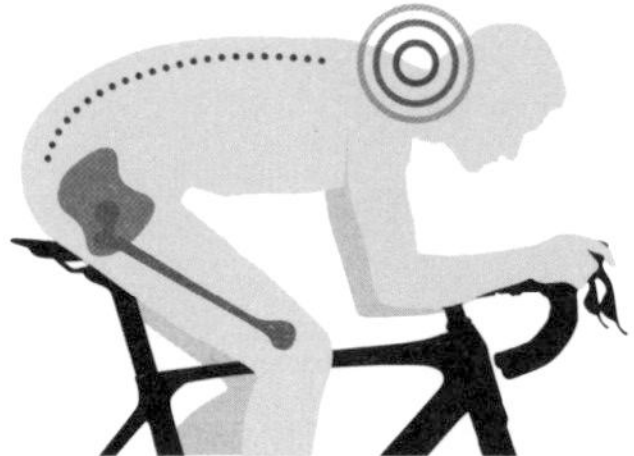

Gradually exposing yourself to bigger challenges strengthens mind and body

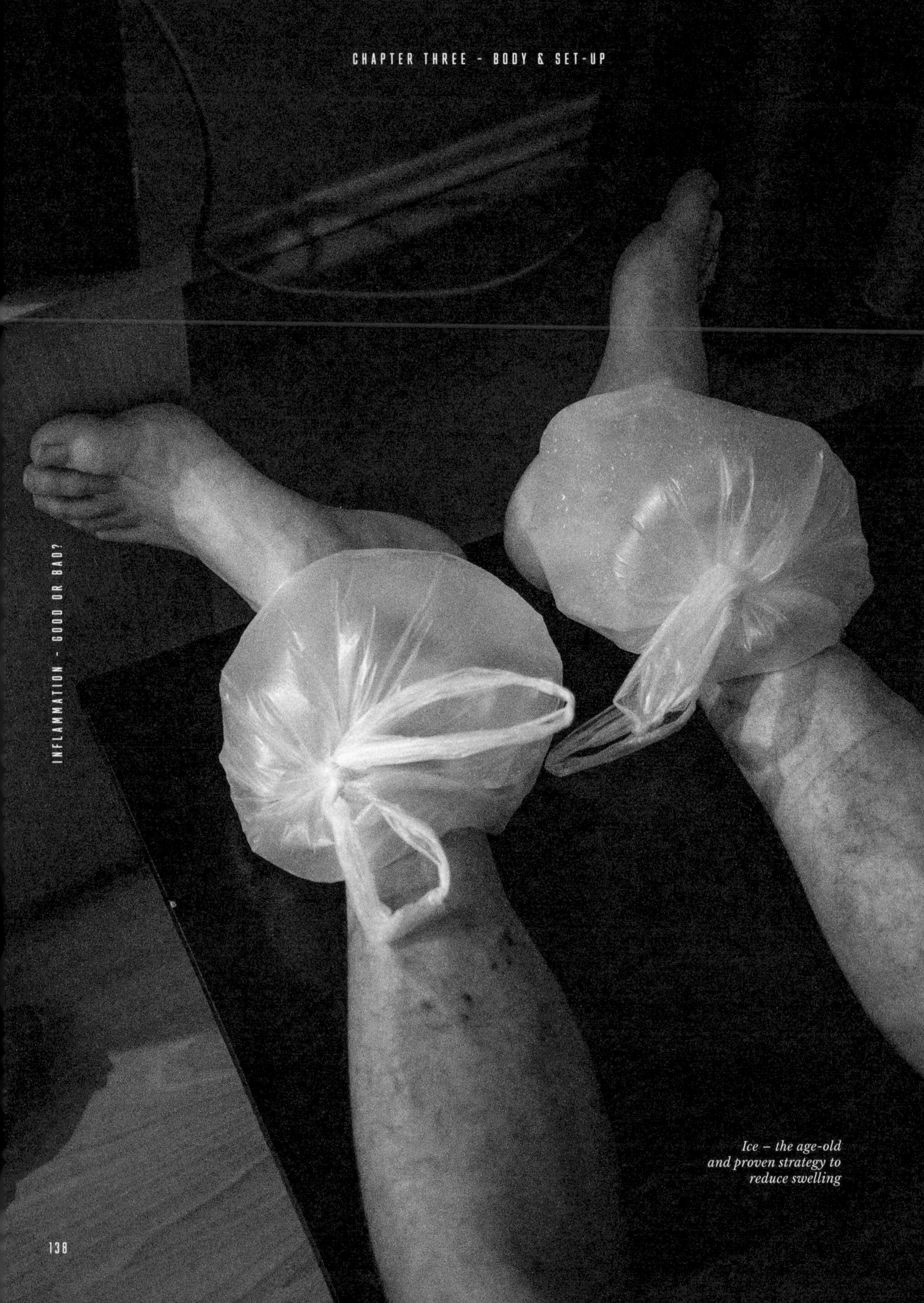

Ice – the age-old and proven strategy to reduce swelling

Chapter Three

INFLAMMATION – GOOD OR BAD?

Your body's natural defence system will optimise recovery from injury, which is why you must be aware of the pros and cons of painkillers

LP | **When you injure yourself, the area often reddens and is warm** and swollen. This is inflammation and is the body's natural method of healing. Take a twisted ankle. This has led to disruption of the ligaments (which connect bone to bone) on the outside of the ankle that provide stability to a joint. By falling on the outside of your ankle, the force has outweighed the tensile capacity of the ligament and it's torn, whether partially or fully ruptured.

"You want to heal naturally, so if you're taking medicine for pain, take paracetamol not ibuprofen"

With this tearing comes further tearing of the microcirculation/vessels, which causes bleeding. This bleeding, depending on how close to the surface it is or how significant the bleed is, will either show up within the first few hours or even over several days. The body's response is to flush the area with fluid containing different types of cells that start the healing process. These chemicals/cells, however, often irritate nerves, which is why inflammation's associated with pain. And it explains how anti-inflammatories like ibuprofen work. Ibuprofen restricts the release of inflammatory cells, like prostaglandins, and so reduces the irritation on specific nerve endings and cuts pain.

The problem is you want the body to heal naturally, so if you're taking medicine for pain, take paracetamol (also known as Tyrenol in other countries including the US). Paracetamol's an analgesic. It works by dampening that painful feeling in the nerves, but doesn't impact the cause of the pain, namely the inflammation.

Risks of anti-inflammatories

In endurance and particularly ultra-endurance, it's strongly advised to avoid ingesting anti-inflammatory medications because they raise the chances of acute kidney injury and failure. This may take some relearning as many cyclists take anti-inflammatories as a precautionary measure. But you can't ignore the risks. I first became aware of these when supporting Mark around the world. Dr Andrew Murray, our supporting sports physician, explained to me a couple of cases he'd seen first-hand.

There are an increasing number of journals on this, too, specifically its impact on ultra-endurance events. →

Hodgson, LE et al (2017) carried out a review of many studies and discovered across five marathons and six ultra-marathons that there were 27 cases of acute kidney injury. The majority didn't experience symptoms for up to a week after the event. In two-thirds of cases, there was a history of non-steroidal anti-inflammatories (NSAID, ie ibuprofen) before and/or during the event.

Inhibiting filtration rate

The problems stem from rhabdomyolysis, which is the breakdown of skeletal muscle, seen in catabolic endurance and ultra-endurance events. This releases myoglobin into the bloodstream. Myoglobin is the protein that stores oxygen in your muscles. Your blood filters through your kidneys, but proteins are a large molecule and not easily filtered, so if you have too much myoglobin in your blood, combined with other stresses such as dehydration and adding medications to be filtered, the combined effect can cause kidney damage by reducing their filtration rate.

Although it's not common, it does happen. Having seen the severity and the long-term implications, we'd strongly recommend avoiding the use of anti-inflammatories during endurance events.

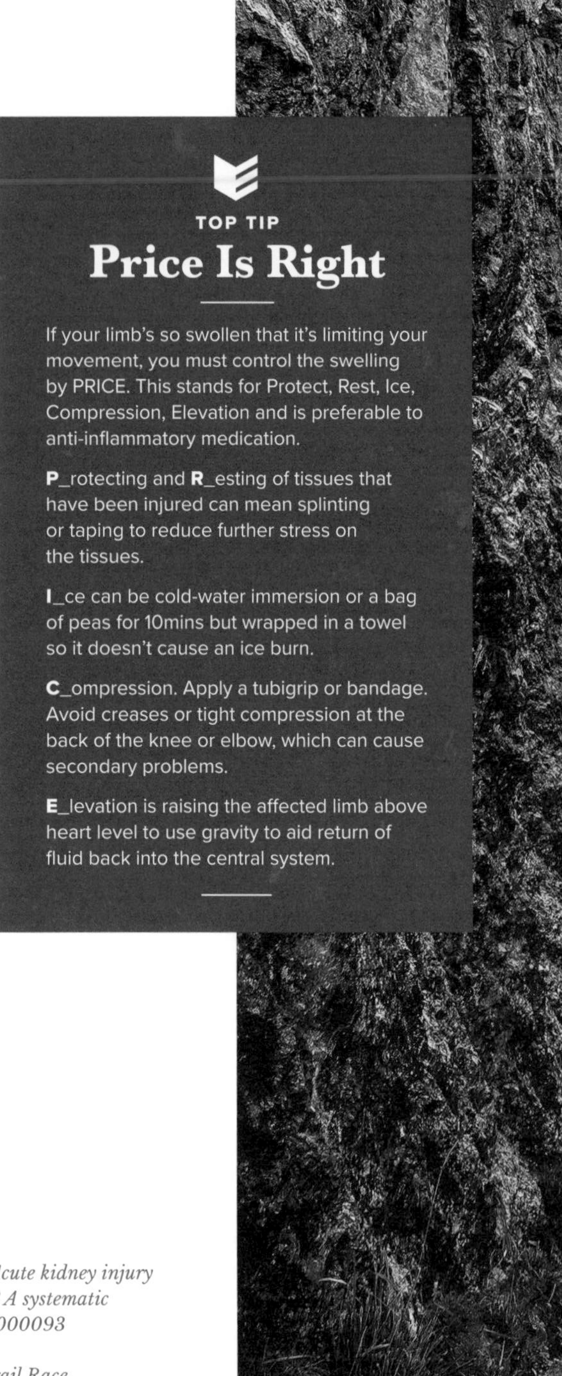

TOP TIP

Price Is Right

If your limb's so swollen that it's limiting your movement, you must control the swelling by PRICE. This stands for Protect, Rest, Ice, Compression, Elevation and is preferable to anti-inflammatory medication.

P_rotecting and **R**_esting of tissues that have been injured can mean splinting or taping to reduce further stress on the tissues.

I_ce can be cold-water immersion or a bag of peas for 10mins but wrapped in a towel so it doesn't cause an ice burn.

C_ompression. Apply a tubigrip or bandage. Avoid creases or tight compression at the back of the knee or elbow, which can cause secondary problems.

E_levation is raising the affected limb above heart level to use gravity to aid return of fluid back into the central system.

References: Hodgson LE, Walter E, Venn RM, et al. (2017) Acute kidney injury associated with endurance events – is it a cause for concern? A systematic review. BMJ Open Sport Exerc Med. doi:10.1136/bmjsem-2015- 000093

Scheer V (April 24, 2020) Severe Kidney Injury After a 110-km Trail Race . Cureus 12(4): e7814. DOI 10.7759/cureus.7814

Avoid anti-inflammatories if you can, especially over a multi-day challenge

Chapter Three

FINAL THOUGHTS_

A whistle-stop tour of what you should apply from this chapter to your own endurance challenge

This chapter's seen us focus on different bike components. We'll reflect on that shortly. Before then, we must also stress that it's good to experiment with bikes. Borrow friends' bikes or try demos. Try gravel if you're used to riding road and vice versa, to give you a better understanding of how different frames' geometries handle, how different tyres grip, and how different bars and saddles feel. Small changes make a massive difference in your comfort and efficiency.

If you remember nothing else from this chapter, log this: drop your elbows. Your elbows neutralise your upper body, allowing your legs to spin more efficiently. It's difficult to drop your elbows and stay tense on the bike!

I'd recommend that you ride compact gears and, given the choice, choose electric. Over big miles and long hours, 'buttons' for gear shifters rather than levers makes a significant difference, especially if you feel the cold or suffer from numbness issues. Also, tri-bars are a worthwhile investment for efficient cycling. They also feel very cool. Mind you, only use tri-bars when riding solo endurance and never within urban areas.

Seek out the right saddle

If you have tri-bars, make sure the saddle's also comfortable when your hips rotate forwards and your weight's on the narrower part. It's easy to find a saddle that's comfortable in one position – either TT or road – but finding one that's equally comfortable in both takes some exploring. Just remember what works for one person might not work for another, as keeping a comfortable backside is as personal as it gets!

For endurance riding, double tape the top section of your bars, until the brake hoods; use insoles that have a degree of cushioning; support your instep; and choose a saddle that also has some cushioning, without being too wide. Don't be tempted by gel saddle covers or anything that makes your saddle resemble a wobbly park bench!

"Your elbows neutralise your upper body, allowing your legs to spin more efficiently. It's difficult to drop your elbows and stay tense on the bike!"

Bulletproof your body on and off the bike with this chapter's essential tips

Chapter Four

THE SCIENCE OF ENDURANCE

You don't require the knowledge of a trained exercise physiologist, but an overview of how your body works will help you train smarter and ride further

Mark and his team calculated he had to average 15mph when riding around the world

Chapter Four

SETTING YOUR BENCHMARK

Knowing the physiological, hormonal and biological factors that'll affect the outcome of your endurance challenge are key to your progress

MB | **Everything in endurance cycling, starts with what you're trying to** achieve. Then you can figure out where to focus your energy. There'll be a performance gap so it's worth training for. If it's not hard and something that inspires you, I doubt you'd be reading a book about endurance.

LP | Before progressing, you must know where your current capabilities are in relation to the performance demands of your goal. Know the gaps! It's then about seeing how to close those gaps, how to prioritise those gains and how long it will take. When it comes to performance areas, we could be talking physiological progress, physical conditioning, psychological preparations, recovery strategies, or injury or illness history management.

Taking an empirical approach to this is beneficial. Say your target's to cover a certain distance in a certain time, then you can calculate what average speed you'll need to sustain in order to reach that goal. This is where you can start to identify your first area of gains – what's your ability to sustain that pace for a given time period? This should then shape your training.

Assess before progress

For Mark's 80 Days, we knew he needed to cover 18,000 miles in 75 days in order to have five days' travel and contingency, meaning an average of 240 miles per day. We wanted him to enjoy a minimum five hours a day of sleep. That left 19 hours. With four x four-hour blocks and 30 minutes' recovery between, this became our achievable strategy. With 16 hours of riding time to cover 240 miles, Mark had to sustain an average of 15mph.

Our first assessment was to see if that was possible. As Mark hadn't long finished cycling the length of Africa, he was comfortable at 15mph. The big change was the duration, almost doubling the time he was on the bike every day.

We then tested his physiology in the lab and examined his blood markers for benchmarks, then determined at what heart rate could Mark sustain for days on end. We could then train specifically to build on this and raise his ability to recover quicker. You may not have access to such detailed sports testing, but you can still apply the same process to your goals through testing and a training plan.

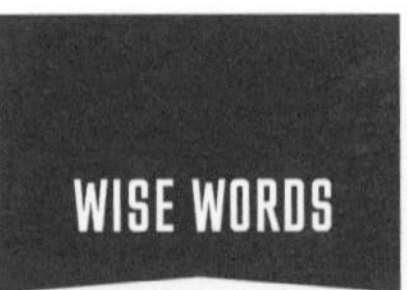

What Defines Endurance?

Once you understand exactly what endurance is, you can set about improving yours

ENDURANCE LESSONS WITH
Expert sport scientist Professor Greg Whyte OBE

Greg Whyte defines endurance as any event lasting over an hour. Ultra-endurance is more an individual call but, for many, it's more than 100 miles.

Mid-term and short-term goals are essential for achieving your long-term goals. Greg works in session-specific goals – what are we going to achieve today? As your neuromuscular system develops, so too will your mentality and physical capacity.

There are three key physiological elements at play that'll determine your success. Firstly, the training plan. Not only is this vital for progress, it also provides a record of all your sessions.

Secondly, 'prehabilitation'. This can be strength and conditioning to avoid injury or ensuring that you're receiving the best nutrition for your development.

Finally, you must optimise your methods of recovery. This means factors like making sure that you're enjoying the right quantity of sleep or at least a good-quality sleep.

Importance of supercompensation
An overload of exercise results in fatigue and an inevitable drop in performance. But sufficient recovery after fatiguing – but not too much – will lead to improvements that are above your baseline when you return to training. This cycle is called

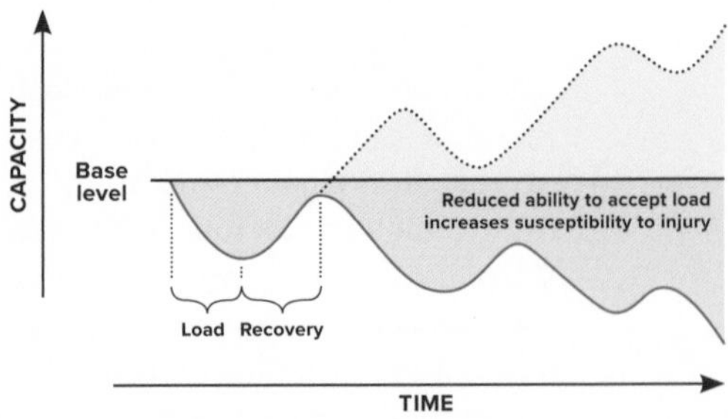

Repeated bouts of training without rest puts you into decline (red). However, train and recover adequately after a block takes you into 'supercompensation' (blue), so you recover ahead of where your baseline was.

Optimal adaptation comes from balancing training output with recovery

"As your neuromuscular system develops, so too will your mentality and physical capacity"

'supercompensation' (see graph, left). Greg recommends inducing fatigue and then, before you've fully recovered, ride again to induce fatigue further still. This is called 'overreaching' and will lead to progressive improvements. Monitoring your performance will lead to consistent gains, so pencil in a key test that you intersperse within your programme. This will tell you two things about your training: whether you're progressing as well as acting as a feedback mechanism for what kind of physical condition you're in.

To hear more listen to the Endurance podcast on Apple Podcasts, Spotify, Google Podcasts, Amazon Music or search for it on your favourite Podcast App.

Chapter Four

RAPID RECOVERY

Understanding – and then applying – repair, rebuild and growth strategies will make the most of every training session

LP | **Recovery is often considered an add-on – something that we** 'should' do rather than 'must' do. But recovery needs to be a key component of training. I often wonder if we changed the word recovery whether we would see greater buy-in? Given we do high-intensity training, low-intensity training and conditioning training, maybe if we aligned it with the word 'training' by calling it 'adaptation training', people would see that it's a segment of training that has to be programmed like every other? Food for thought.

Part of recovery is rest; when we rest, our body comes alive on a cellular level if we've been pushing it hard. It's a time that the body can heal and adapt from within. When I've completed a 24-hour cycle, unless I've overcooked it, then my body screams out for sleep afterwards and I enjoy the best eight to nine hours of sleep for the next couple of days. And if I can't give it the full sleep block, then I'll add in the cat naps, which feel amazing when I wake up (more on sleep later in this chapter).

Train hard, recover smart

It's long been known in exercise physiology that applying a stress – in this case, long bike rides – with sufficient recovery time maximises adaptation. Essentially, we must put our bodies through enough stress to cause breakdown, but then provide adequate rest to allow the muscles to recover and adapt to become stronger than before. Without it, you're just depleting the system, constantly on a downward spiral or stressing the tissues to the point that they'll fail.

Failed recovery over time will present itself in injury, illness or under performance. For the 80 Days project we couldn't risk any of these, but we knew Mark would be going into decline throughout the world and my only blocks of recovery windows were the long-haul flights. We had to maximise the windows overnight between each day of riding and the 15 to 30 minutes between each →

"We must put our bodies through enough stress to cause breakdown, but then provide adequate rest to allow the muscles to recover and adapt to become stronger than before"

Massage is beneficial but don't neglect the basics like time management and sleep

Mark utilises high-tech recovery tools, like pneumatic compression

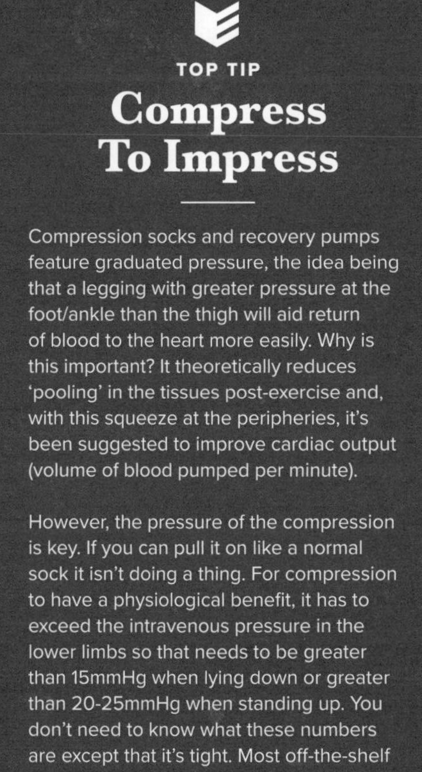

TOP TIP

Compress To Impress

Compression socks and recovery pumps feature graduated pressure, the idea being that a legging with greater pressure at the foot/ankle than the thigh will aid return of blood to the heart more easily. Why is this important? It theoretically reduces 'pooling' in the tissues post-exercise and, with this squeeze at the peripheries, it's been suggested to improve cardiac output (volume of blood pumped per minute).

However, the pressure of the compression is key. If you can pull it on like a normal sock it isn't doing a thing. For compression to have a physiological benefit, it has to exceed the intravenous pressure in the lower limbs so that needs to be greater than 15mmHg when lying down or greater than 20-25mmHg when standing up. You don't need to know what these numbers are except that it's tight. Most off-the-shelf garments don't apply this pressure and are more for fashion than function. Bespoke compression garments are best for an effective physiological benefit.

"If you're not sleeping and eating well, the effects of compression garments are going to be minimal"

four-hour block. A good example of where recovery proved beneficial was when Mark started presenting with a cough after cycling over a long stretch of dusty road. It grew persistent and we couldn't shift it for the next two weeks across Russia and into China. It wasn't until he got on the plane, slept for eight hours straight, had a ton of fresh food, that when he arrived in Australia there was no cough!

The order of preference and biggest gains you can make from recovery are:

1 – **Programme planning and time management**
2 – **Sleep**
3 – **Nutrition**
4 – **Mobility**
5 – **Extras.** These are things like soft-tissue treatment, contrast bathing, compression clothing and muscle stimulation.

Like everything else we've talked about in this book, the foundations are key to reaching your endurance goals. For example, if you're not sleeping and eating well, the effects of wearing compression garments are going to be minimal. In order to sleep well and eat well, you need to plan your week and be prepared. If you listen to our podcast with Professor Greg Whyte OBE, he summarises this simply as, 'You can't polish a turd!'

Chapter Four

THE SCIENCE OF SLEEP

Sleep really is the best medicine when it comes to riding strong and far every day

LP | **Sleep scientist Dr Luke Gupta explains why sleep is vital to aid** recovery. 'Sleep provides time to allow certain hormone levels to rise,' he says. 'This allows your body to grow.' Growth hormones are released in high levels during sleep, providing the building blocks to aid tissue recovery and growth. That growth's maximised by adequate nutrition before you sleep and on waking.

This is all well and good, of course, but practically, what does a good night's sleep look like? And how can you raise your chances of enjoying a fruitful, refreshing, performance-boosting sleep?

— **Duration:** it's an individual thing but, broadly speaking, a daily seven to nine hours' sleep is the ideal. If you're sleeping less, try and nap during the day.

— **Sleep reactivity:** falling asleep within 20 minutes and going back to sleep easily if you wake in the night.

— **Sleep quality:** an easy way to gauge this is if you're waking up refreshed?

— **Forget tech:** forget monitors and listen to your own body.

— **Fuel well:** combine restorative nutrition around your sleep to optimise your recovery window.

TOP TIP

Sleep Easy, Ride Strong

Studies show that consecutive nights of poor sleep lowers power output and impacts decision making. So to sleep that bit better and ride stronger...

- Optimum room temperature for sleep is 16-19°C. Create a warm microclimate around you with a duvet or blankets.
- Your core body temperature drops overnight, so a warm bath one to two hours before you go to bed has been shown to improve sleep.
- Timing of food consumption impacts quality of sleep, so a protein-carb shake might be more beneficial after a late session than a big meal.
- Ban caffeine after 4pm (unless you're riding through the night).
- Turn off the tech an hour or two before bed.
- Muscle soreness after a heavy session can keep you awake, which is why recovery strategies can be beneficial.

Smartphones stimulate your brain, so are a definite no-no when seeking sleep

Lack of sleep leads to reduced power output and poor decision making

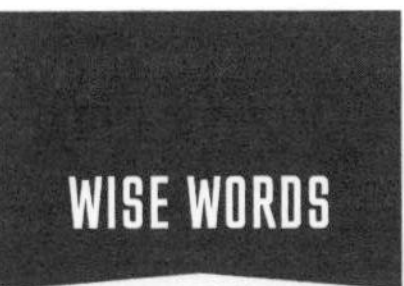

The Importance Of Sleep

It's the most natural of activities but do we really know why we sleep?

ENDURANCE LESSONS WITH
Sleep expert Dr Charlotte Elsworth-Edelsten

Why exactly do we sleep? 'We sleep to stay alive! If we didn't sleep at all (including no micro naps) for more than eight days, we'd die,' explains Charlotte. We have two processes that make us sleep, says Charlotte: 'One is our pressure to sleep. The longer we're awake, the sleepier we feel. But we also have the circadian rhythm, which is our biological functions oscillating around a 24-hour period, and that's hugely controlled by light and dark.'

Stress affecting sleep

'There's a concept called sleep reactivity, which is how vulnerable your sleep is to stress. There's also a daytime alertness aspect – some people are just 'alert' people. Even under experiences of sleep deprivation they don't experience sleepiness in the same way. There's innate physiology that's very human, but there are individual differences within that. For some people, sleep just doesn't come easily and there's a genetic element to that.'

LP | Personally, I know I can 'survive' on minimal sleep having spent nine months at sea, sleeping for only 90 minutes at a time. However, can we truly 'perform' on minimal sleep? The answer to that depends on what the performance requires. For me I needed to row, eat, sleep, repeat, but I'd regularly have strong hallucinations in the twilight hours when my body was screaming out for me to shut my eyes. I also couldn't focus on more than one thing at a time and was operating like a robot with little thought. For road cycling, you have an added issue of staying safe on the road – greater cognitive importance to being able to react, which are the very factors that go when severely sleep deprived.

To hear more, listen to the Endurance podcast on Apple Podcasts, Spotify, Google Podcasts, Amazon Music or search for it on your favourite podcast app.

Chapter Four

CLOSING OF THE GENDER GAP

Physiological differences mean the longer the distance, the stronger female riders become. Why? Let us explain...

LP | **Fifty years ago, feats of endurance were mainly** undertaken by males. It was the same at the Olympics with only 20% of competitors female in 1960. Even now, high-profile events like the Tour de France are male only (at least in its 21-stage format). But things are changing. High-profile athletes using their platform to cite inequality plus greater investment means things are improving slowly. But

"In 2019, Jasmin Paris became the first woman to win the 268-mile Montane Spine Race"

in endurance, things are changing far more rapidly. At all levels and in many disciplines of endurance, females have not only closed the gap on males but taken the lead...

In 2019, Jasmin Paris became the first woman to win the 268-mile Montane Spine Race. Lael Wilcox won the Trans Am Bike Race in 2016 and set the course record for the Tour Divide. Fiona Kolbinger won the Transcontinental Race in 2019, beating a field of 224 men and 40 women. Sarah Thomas set the world record for the longest, unassisted outdoor swim at 104.6 miles in 2017.

Endurance – the leveller

It's impressive stuff and not only highlights the individual determination of each of these athletes, but also that endurance is a great leveller. When it comes to sprints and power events, males continue to lead the way. Go long – especially to ultra-endurance – and it's a different picture. Why? The theories are multifactorial. Firstly, there's an age-related idea. Long endurance events tend to attract the older age group of individuals; the largest age group in endurance cycling is 45-49. This is important because, as we age, there are hormonal changes that influence performance. Testosterone's understood in males, yet there are other hormones which are equally as influential on a female's performance, such as oestrogen and progesterone (see p162, 'Wise Words: The Female Athlete' for more detail).

Alongside hormonal and metabolic differences, there are also variations in the dominance of muscle-fibre type, therefore making an individual more suited to either power based versus endurance-based activity, which is contributed by individual →

Fiona Kolbinger won the Transcontinental Race. Surprise? Science says not

Women generally have better self-care routines, which pays off in ultra-endurance

differences in our neuromuscular make-up (the nervous system which stimulates a muscle to contract).

It's not just physical differences – there's the psychological element, too. In Chapter Two we talked about the 'ability to endure' but there's also the considerations of different personality traits, those that are intrinsically versus extrinsically driven in their motivations. This is applicable to both sexes but research shows that females show a greater proportion of being intrinsically driven than men, meaning they're predominantly more self-critical and more motivated by competing against themselves than others.

Something more rudimentary that often separates the genders when it comes to endurance is that of hygiene and self-care. When rowing the Pacific Ocean, one element that helped my team and I endure was paying keen attention to hygiene and routines. However, the number of males that I interviewed, met with or read books about during our preparations who didn't place importance on their hygiene routines and then experienced horrific salt sores was significant. That was unless they came from a military background.

That's why it's important we highlight the female-specific factors that need to be considered when training for an ultra-endurance event. And also highlight the advantages females and males naturally have – and what we can learn from each other.

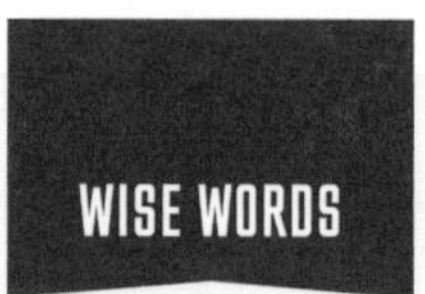

The Female Athlete

Biological and hormonal awareness will help the female rider optimise their training rides

ENDURANCE LESSONS WITH
Women's health and performance expert Dr Emma Ross

While working at the EIS (English Institute of Sport), Dr Emma Ross asked a number of practitioners whether they altered their approach depending on their athlete's gender. Overwhelmingly, the answer was no. These were coaches who'd been successful with males and were seeing the same positive results with their female clients.

But something's not right here. There are such fundamental differences in the physiology, anatomy, biomechanics and psychology of men and women that it simply didn't make sense that they weren't doing more to support women as both 'female' and 'athlete'.

There's no clearer example of the physiological difference between males and females than the menstrual cycle, which, as I'll detail, influences your performance. Women have two predominant sex hormones: oestrogen and progesterone. Across an average 28-day cycle, these hormones ebb and flow. In the first five days, the production of both hormones is low, after which oestrogen rises significantly. This is the stage just before women ovulate. The influence of this hormone, in an evolutionary sense, is to go out and find a mate. In the second half of the cycle, after the egg's been produced, progesterone is released. This induces a feeling of calm in preparation to nurture the potentially fertilised egg.

In contrast, men have it relatively straight-forward. They have a cyclical release of testosterone that peaks in the morning and declines throughout the day. This repeats throughout their life, declining over time. →

"Come the second half of the cycle, hormone levels help women metabolise fat more efficiently"

Ultra rider Jenny Graham epitomises an important four-letter word – GRIT

High levels of oestrogen increases serotonin, which motivates riders to train

WISE WORDS

Hormones, Emma stresses, aren't an obstacle to performance. But to train optimally they need to be worked with, not against. In the first half of the cycle, for instance, the influx of oestrogen increases levels of serotonin, which can motivate people to train and maximise high-intensity exercise. It also aids digestion and recovery. Come the second half of the cycle, hormone levels enable women to metabolise fat more efficiently. That's why it's the perfect time to schedule longer sessions.

There's also a growing belief that if women do more strength training in the first half of their cycle, they enjoy greater adaptation. That's because oestrogen increases growth hormone in response to exercise and influences the ability to recover. There's also evidence that it reduces muscle soreness.

Recent studies suggest that the menstrual cycle has no effect on a woman's performance capacities. Aerobic capacity, lactate threshold and strength measurements are consistent throughout the cycle. However, just because the capacities are the same doesn't mean that they can be accessed in the same way. Not only can hormones affect motivation, they can also cause physical symptoms such as gastro distress. That means if you're prone to gastrointestinal distress at certain stages of the month, you should adjust your diet on those days by consuming really simple foods.

It's also important to highlight that hormonal profiles change over time. There are significant changes between adolescence, fertility, pregnancy, post-natal, perimenopause and menopause. Emma reflects that her period never used to cause her the slightest concern. She regularly competed in ultra-endurance and was never once made overly aware of her body's fluctuating hormone levels. However, shortly after the birth of her first child, she started experiencing symptoms similar to stomach flu: diarrhoea, stomach cramps, nausea and fever. After about a day, it'd stop. She went to her doctor, who was so perplexed he sent her to the tropical medicine department. It wasn't until she went to a female GP that she learnt the symptoms were connected to her cycle.

All in all, there's an enormous opportunity to ameliorate the performances of female athletes simply by paying attention and doing the research. It's time to be smarter – and that goes for everyone.

To hear more, listen to the Endurance podcast on Apple Podcasts, Spotify, Google Podcasts, Amazon Music or search for it on your favourite podcast app.

Chapter Four

FINAL THOUGHTS_

Essential takeaways to apply to your own riding

We've reached the end of our scientific journey. We've highlighted how an understanding of your anatomy and physiology will crank up your riding to another level. In the next chapter, we give you the training specifics to stretch your stamina and power up your pedalling. But before then, let's just recap in a little more detail what we've learnt...

Become A Holistic Rider

Understanding your performance gap – where you can improve to make you a stronger ride – will help you to direct your training programme. But don't forget to support the riding load with adequate conditioning, injury prevention and recovery strategies.

Trust Your Body

Become body literate. While you should use them, don't become a slave to your computers and monitors. Regularly train on 'feel' for a good, long ride, so you figure out what subtle changes you can make to influence intrinsically, rather than be driven by numbers 24/7. Your body will give you signs of fatigue before your watch does. Remember that 'mood' is a better predictor than any computer. Be intuitive with how you feel after sleep.

Keep A Trace

That said, keep a record of your training sessions so you can look back and understand if a drop in performance is planned and expected because you're over-reaching versus an unexpected under performance and risk of it being because of relative energy deficiency (REDS). You can do this via an app or a good-old fashioned training diary.

Female-Specific Training

As a female athlete, think about how you can train smarter and develop more intuitive ways of training specifically to get the best out of yourself.

Recover Like A Pro

Recovery is often the missing link in endurance training. Yes you need to endure, yes you need to train hard, but you also need to train smart – and that means balancing stress and rest.

"Your body will give you signs of fatigue before your watch does. Remember that 'mood' is the best predictor than any computer"

Keeping a record of your sessions will help you tweak training load

Chapter Five

TRAINING FOR ENDURANCE

Yes, you can just get out there and pedal. But being more structured with your rides plus focussing on strength work will lead to much greater results

Push yourself harder in training than during your ride to 'bulletproof' yourself

Chapter Five

TRAIN HARD, RECOVER WELL, RACE STRONG

Digging deep in sessions will bulletproof your mind and body come your challenge

MB | **Many people could wing it without training on a shorter** ride, especially one that lacks intensity. But as you edge towards the century ride and beyond – especially multi-day – very few people can pull these rides out of the bag without consistent training. However, from sitting on a couch, eating chips and watching boxsets, I'd challenge anyone to cycle 100 miles if they had 12 weeks and were committed to the training.

Gone are the days when endurance cyclists just go out and turn over steady, low-intensity miles thinking it would strengthen the aerobic system (your energy system that needs oxygen to function). We know that you need variety in your training to not only keep it interesting, but to test your body in different ways and build the conditioning to endure longer hours. And bear in mind that conditioning isn't the same as fitness. Your muscles and tendons can be strong, but to endure on long rides brings in the nervous system, flexibility, form and ability to mentally cope with longer hours.

Sustainable speed

I push it much harder in training than I'd ever push myself on an endurance ride. By that I mean I go deeper, seeing spikes in heart rate and power that I'd never risk during the event that I'm training for. That's because the endurance bike rider is always protecting themselves for tomorrow, making their ride sustainable. You don't have the luxury of riding to fail as if it was a 25-mile time-trial.

When I cycled around the world, in general I kept my power output under 200 watts to protect myself. Into the hills and headwinds is the only time I closely watched the power meter so as not to overcook it. Which begs the question: why did I push it so hard in training? Well, raising your functional threshold (roughly the average power output you can hold for an hour) via intervals, hills and pyramids means that your →

"Into the hills and headwinds is the only time I closely watched the power meter so as not to overcook it"

"I train using a traditional three-weeks build, one-week recovery pattern"

FTP (funcational threshold power) might increase from, say, 280 watts to 320 watts. Why's that important? When it comes to your challenge, sitting on a nice 150 watts, for example, will feel easier if your FTP's 320 watts as it's a lower percentage of your maximum. If you always train at the same intensity, training on a route that doesn't really put you into the red, you'll find extending this effort much harder.

But there is a balance. Road racers often assume that just because they can 'smash it', that they'll also be able to slow down and 'do' endurance. But I know many riders with very impressive top-end power and a fierce sprint who struggle to ride a double-century. It's both a physical and mental issue.

Progress and recover

As for me, I train using a traditional three-weeks build, one-week recovery pattern. There are many different ways to split your training calendar, but this works for me. It gives me a week each month to rebuild and strengthen my immune system, and reduce the stress on my muscular and nervous systems. Importantly, it gives me a mental break from feeling sore, too! However many hours you might train for your goal challenge, this is a beneficial way to plan your training. (This is all about the idea of supercompensation, which we focussed on in Chapter Four.)

Raising your functional threshold will make endurance rides feel easier

For most endurance riders, family's the most important time to protect outside of training

Chapter Five

PROGRAMME PLANNING

Your goal requires balancing training with the rest of your life. It's time to work out your priorities

LP | **Programme planning and time management's often overlooked.** I'm not just talking about your training plans here – I'm talking about life for all the moments you are awake and asleep.

When I started to work with Mark, it became clear that this'd be the greatest area of gains to ensure he started the 80 Days best prepared. Mark's a husband and father of two young girls, who runs his own business. He flies all over the world, while being an endurance cyclist that doesn't get out of bed for a ride of less than four hours. He was also leading the 80 Days project, co-ordinating the sponsorship, the team, the charity... Basically, Mark was wired on adrenaline fumes from day one of us meeting! So we sat down and discussed the following questions while populating a calendar:

— **What's the most important time to protect outside of training?** For instance, time with the family.

— **To protect this, what's the minimal time that you'd feel comfortable with?** Protecting some breakfast times and some bed times a week with the kids, and one full day off at the weekend for family.

— **What are the non-negotiable work commitments?**

— **What's the travel time and mode of travel for these commitments?**

— **Are there any key social engagements/dates in the diary that you're committed to?**

That last one's more important than you might think. You'll make many sacrifices and test your physical capacity through all the training, so it's important to keep some social engagements to reboot your mental energy and ensure you've got things to look forward to.

Pencil in training targets

Once you've answered the above type of questions and your calendar is nicely populated, you then overlay your training targets...

— **What are your big milestones to check you're on or off track?** For the 80 Days we set the Around Britain challenge to complete two weeks of back-to-back 240 miles per day. In order to be ready for Around Britain, we needed to ensure Mark had completed at least four separate 240-mile rides. To be ready for a 240-mile day of four x four-hour →

blocks, he needed to have completed two x four-hour blocks before that, working up from single four-hour rides. When it comes to you, ask yourself...

— **Where will these milestones be best placed in the calendar to ensure you're ready for these checkpoints and you have adequate recovery off the back?**

— **How do these milestones sit alongside your earlier commitments?**

To prepare for these milestones, what's the minimum time required per week for the following...?
— Time needed to prep nutrition
— Time of long riding and low intensity
— Time of high-intensity riding
— Time of recovery management
— Time of treatment and rehabilitation
— Total time of strength and conditioning.

— **Populate your weekly diary with your training alongside your work/family/ social commitments and see what needs shifting. Can you achieve your minimal training targets per week?** If not, decide what you can sacrifice that week that you can give back another time.

— **If there's no wiggle room, what's the order of priority in your training that you have to ensure you complete your goal challenge?** For example, if you're a crit cyclist who's signed up to do LEJOG (Land's End to John O'Groats), you need to prioritise your weakness (long rides) that week at expense of your high-intensity sessions (strengths).

Fill your diary with training, family and work commitments

"Where will the milestones be best placed in the calendar to ensure you're ready for these checkpoints?"

Chapter Five

PERIODISATION OF TRAINING

Varying the intensity of your training will reap big rewards come your endurance challenge

MB | **The traditional road-racer approach to training is to build** steady base miles over the winter, then increase intensity over the spring ready for a summer of races. If you're targeting century rides, multi-day endurance or days in the mountains, do the opposite – reverse periodisation. This is where intensity levels are high over the winter and into the spring, and where turbo sessions come into their own. You then ease the intensity, building conditioning for endurance as the weather improves and you can ride outside more. This results in sustaining a higher power output for longer at your event.

The two most common types of session an endurance rider should focus on are long, low-intensity rides (zone two, endurance, see 'In the Zone' box, p181) and shorter rides with relatively long intervals (zone three, tempo). When training for 80 Days, my low-intensity rides were often 12 hours long; the shorter sessions with intervals were three to four hours. For you, the long rides may be four hours, while the shorter rides – with roughly 20 minute intervals – may be one to two hours. Your training needs to be appropriate to your target events.

"You shouldn't try and simply ride by numbers without an awareness of how you feel"

Measuring progress

Perceived effort, using the Rate of Perceived Exertion (RPE) scale where one is easy and 10 is very hard, is a useful way to self measure, which you can support with heart-rate and/or power data. Don't fall into the trap of simply riding by numbers without an awareness of how you feel. Mould them together and you paint a complete picture of your effort, recovery, health and energy levels.

FTP is important. It's a test that you can complete on any bike with a power meter and is 95% of your 20-minute best effort, which represents your ability to sustain your highest power over an hour. Note your average power output for this test, multiply by 0.95 and that gives you your FTP. For accuracy – and when recovered – a follow-up test is to take that 95% figure and see if you can actually sustain it for an hour. Mind over matter, this hurts, but is great for building discipline.

Once you know your FTP, you can set your training zones. It's important to train through the range to increase ⟶

Taking 95% of your power output over your 20-minute best effort gives you your FTP

If feasible, ride your predicted event time in training. Time's more important than distance

efficiency and, in turn, the average power and speed you can sustain over long periods of time. However, as I mentioned at the start, the two key zones for an endurance rider are zones two (endurance) and three (tempo). So let's dig a little deeper into those.

Zone two is 56-75% of your FTP and about 69-83% of your average heart rate (HR) during an FTP test (e.g. if it's 170bpm during a test, your zone two would be 117-141bpm). It's designed to build a strong aerobic base, which is what you'll need over endurance challenges. It also lets you recover between higher-intensity efforts, like a mountain climb.

The longer these zone-two rides can be, the greater the adaptation you'll enjoy.

In The Zone

Training schedules should be measurable, so pencil in regular tests, ideally once a month. This could be an indoor test, like the FTP (detailed on the next page), or simply time taken on a local training ride.

Remember to be realistic. Even training for 80 Days I couldn't fit in four to six hours' training every day. It just wasn't practical. So to then jump to riding 16 hours a day, every day, for two-and-a-half months meant I needed a strong base. The first few days of the challenge were particularly crucial in terms of injury prevention. On multi-day or week events, this is when repetitive strain injuries normally happen, so you need to ride conservatively.

Polarised training is a popular method of training and will really build your endurance base. It's where 70-80% of sessions are at a low intensity and 20-30% of sessions are at a high intensity, avoiding too much work at mid-range efforts.

Training zones are an easy way to conceptualise effort, whether that's your perceived effort, heart rate or power. The likes of TrainingPeaks (training software) use seven power zones (see below) and was originally developed by Dr Andrew Coggan.

During winter, a combination of zone four lactate threshold sessions, zone three tempo and zone two endurance rides will lay a solid base to build towards your event. Most of your training should be outside but indoor turbo sessions have their place, like they did for my 80 Days.

If using a turbo, an early morning aerobic ride could be done before breakfast to encourage fat adaption (more about that next chapter). Interval training is also easier to stick to indoors, where you don't have traffic lights and changing terrain to deal with, whereas long aerobic rides are much more enjoyable outside.

Training zones

Zone	% of FTP	% FTP HR	Description
Zone 1	0-55	0-68	Active recovery
Zone 2	56-75	69-83	Endurance
Zone 3	76-90	84-94	Tempo
Zone 4	91-105	95-105	Lactate threshold
Zone 5	106-120	> 106	VO_2 max
Zone 6	121-150	N/A	Anaerobic capacity
Zone 7	151+	N/A	Neuromuscular power

"Initially, you should complete tempo intervals and endurance rides on different days"

But this needs to be progressive over time, so your 'normal' for endurance increases over the months. You shouldn't just go out and push a six-hour 'endurance training pace' if you haven't built towards it.

Zone-three benefits

Zone three (84-94% of your threshold heart rate and about 76-90% of your FTP) is about lifting your endurance pace. It really stretches your aerobic boundaries – so much so that it elevates your anaerobic threshold, too, as it's the exertion level between aerobic and anaerobic (see p212 for more on energy systems) training. This is why it's best done in intervals – you'll sustain the right intensity and better-quality work if you ease off slightly between tempo reps. If you don't have any numbers to go off – either power or heart rate – then these sessions should feel like a seven out of 10 on a scale of perceived effort.

Like zone two efforts, zone three tempo work should be integrated throughout the year, during all phases of reverse periodisation. I enjoy repeated 15-minute blocks with lower-intensity efforts in-between; in fact, these 15-minute blocks often tip over into zones four and five. That's fine because while our focus might be heavily on zones two and three, touching upon all zones will improve your endurance performance. Just note that when it comes to intervals, as the set gets tougher, you must retain discipline to keep your efforts consistent.

Initially, complete tempo intervals and endurance rides on different days. For example, you could have sessions during the week where you do a one-hour ride, which include a tempo interval or two. Then at the weekend, go for a longer ride of more than three hours. Once fitness grows, you can then build in the tempo intervals as part of the longer rides. This combination pushes your overall endurance pace whilst also increasing your confidence and physical ability to cope with challenges within the ride.

The 'mock ride'

There's a mindset in marathon running that your longest training run 'only' needs to be around 20 miles because event-day enthusiasm will carry you through the 'domain', which is defined as that tough final third. For cycling, especially if building towards your first major endurance event, you should ride the distance in training to know how it feels and to practise your nutrition strategy (more on this in Chapter Six).

For multi-day and week challenges, you can't replicate the duration of the whole ride, but can ride a day or two of similar hours in the saddle. I call this the 'mock ride'. If your aim's a single-day endurance ride, like a sportive, cycle the distance

Over time, you can build in tempo intervals to your longer endurance rides

or predicted duration even if you can't replicate the elevation gain. Estimated 'time in the saddle' is more important than how far you ride, which'll be dictated by factors like terrain and wind.

If you're goal event's a multi-day ride, there are more variables to practise, including your evening routine off the bike, recovery strategy and knowing what it feels like to get back on the bike in the morning. This could be a weekend effort or, ideally, a three-dayer by tagging on either the Friday or Monday. Things to practise include fuelling within 20 minutes of getting off your bike; prioritising hygiene; and actioning processes around charging kit and checking your bike. It means you'll be physically prepared for day two, albeit you need to experience it to deal with the second-day slump, which many riders struggle with. Also, look to reduce stop times in training and your event. This is a massive take-home for endurance riding.

Finally, when it comes to the challenge itself, your pace will generally vary between 30 and 70% of FTP – a 50-mile sportive rider might ride at the upper end, a multi-dayer the lower end. As you can see, this is lower than many training efforts, but clearly there'll be sections where it's higher like stiff climbs.

It's a lot easier to train consistently if you mix up your landscapes

Chapter Five

READING THE TERRAIN

You don't need to go looking for the hurt with endurance. Rest assured, it will find you!

MB | **Racing over short distances is about power, speed and tactics.** When it comes to endurance and ultra-endurance, you're aiming to make the ride more sustainable. If multi-day, you're also factoring in sleep and recovery. But for this section, we'll focus on when you're riding the bike – how you cover the ground as efficiently as possible.

Pacing's important in terms of setting out slower than feels necessary – I always joke, the hurt from endurance will find you! You should cruise the downhills. When it comes to climbing, pre-empt the extra strain by shifting down the gears. This ability to keep the legs turning at the same tempo is about reading the terrain, especially when riding off-road. Don't attack; when it comes to endurance rides, play the long game.

Endurance riding should be at an effort level where you can maintain conversation. Perceived exertion is far more important when it comes to endurance riding than what your heart rate or power meter tell you.

Ride by perceived exertion

Taking on an endurance ride is different for different people but, using perceived exertion, on a scale of one to 10 for endurance rides I'd call a century ride a five, whereas you might call it a 10 based on your experience. So, let's assume a ride that's between five and 10 mentally and physically stretches you. On this kind of ride, mental preparation is key, thinking through the entire ride so you have a 'psychological arc' set up in your mind. Keeping ahead of nutrition and hydration is your next most important input.

And, of course, we return to pacing. You want to ride even splits (so, for instance, a 100-miler broken down as 10 laps of 10 miles, each roughly the same) or, ideally, reverse splits (where you quicken up), so don't burn too many matches early on in the ride.

Using heart rate (HR) and power are useful checks, but use them more as limiters so that on hills or into a headwind you don't go 'into the red'.

A fun game that I play on the bike is to visualise the road in front of me like a giant pump track, trying to carry as much speed and riding as smoothly as possible, by using as little energy as possible. Especially in varied terrain, this steadies your body, minimises braking and encourages early gear changes.

You'll ride further and faster outdoors by utlising indoor training during the winter

Chapter Five

TURBO SESSIONS & PYRAMIDS _

Playing around with power output and cadence will make you a stronger rider

MB | **For your winter- and spring-intensity training, check out the** amazing library of GCN training videos on YouTube. I've often used these to keep hard training sessions fun and also force myself to stick to a plan.

There are countless options when it comes to designing turbo-trainer sessions. This book's aim isn't to be prescriptive, as everyone will have their own event plans and depth of experience. If you can't find what you need to structure your training programme, it's worth speaking to a coach or research beyond this book.

That said, I'm happy to describe the following three sessions as they're my essentials. Each comprises a training pyramid that involves cadence and power drills...

1 **Varies power, maintains cadence**
2 **Varies cadence, maintains power**
3 **Varies cadence and power**

I enjoy building these types of sessions into my programme for many different reasons. For instance, the power sessions really stretch my mental discipline, while the cadence sessions improve my fluidity and leg speed.

Power session

This session involves riding pyramids at a normal cadence (80-90rpm). Every few minutes you up the resistance but try to keep the same cadence, then down and repeat. Start at what feels like →

"When it comes to cadence, spinning faster for a given speed results in less muscle fatigue"

a fairly easy spin – I'd often start at 200 watts, but you might be more or less than this – and then increase your power by 10 or 20 watts every few minutes until your cadence starts to slow, then back down. Your pyramid will be steeper, and therefore shorter, if you take bigger steps in power. Twice up and down the pyramid will be enough – three if you're feeling strong – with a solid 10-minute warm-up and warm-down. This is great for training steady cadence at different levels of resistance, while concentrating on pedalling smoothness.

Cadence session

Increasing your cadence will take months of focus because you're retraining muscle memory and breaking years of ingrained pedalling habits. But persevere as it makes a massive difference to your speed, fluidity and preservation of energy.

Cadence pyramids start from a normal cadence (90rpm) and then increase by 5rpm every few minutes. Keep resistance the same, stopping your pyramid before you start bobbing and moving around in the saddle. Then head back down through your cadence but keeping your power the same. Starting out, you'll likely be comfortable reaching 110-120rpm before losing stability. The more experienced rider can go up in steps of 10 as you'll likely reach 140-160rpm. For both, choose a power level that you can maintain throughout.

Improving your cadence improves efficiency. While there's no magic number when it comes to cadence, spinning faster for a given speed results in less muscle fatigue. It might feel good to grind out a big gear at the start of a hill but, in similar fashion to lifting a heavy weight in the gym, →

TRAIN WITH GCN

30-Minute Cadence Workout

AEROBIC CADENCE SESSION
TRAIN WITH TEAM SKY

This is an indoor training session to increase your power using four blocks of cadence drills: five minutes at 85% of FTP at a very low cadence, around 45-55rpm; five minutes at 85% of FTP at a much higher cadence, between 90-100rpm; five minutes at 85% of FTP at a low cadence again; final five minutes at 85% of FTP, again at a high cadence, but with the last 20 seconds ridden as hard as you possibly can!

WATCH FOR FREE – https://gcn.eu/4pP

Increasing cadence takes time but persevere – it'll boost speed and efficiency

Widening your cadence bandwidth will make you a stronger all-round cyclist

you have less reps in you than if you were to lift a small weight.

Another cadence idea is 'spin ups' to increase your leg speed. Sticking in the same gear, do 10 bursts of a minute

"One further idea (to improve cadence) is to borrow or hire a fixie or singlespeed and go to the track"

where you accelerate your legs to their maximum cadence without rocking. This will be between 120 and 150rpm. Have sufficient rest to recover well between bursts.

One further idea is to borrow or hire a fixie or singlespeed bike and go to the track. They take some practice – especially the fixie – but it's worth it, as they really focus on cadence.

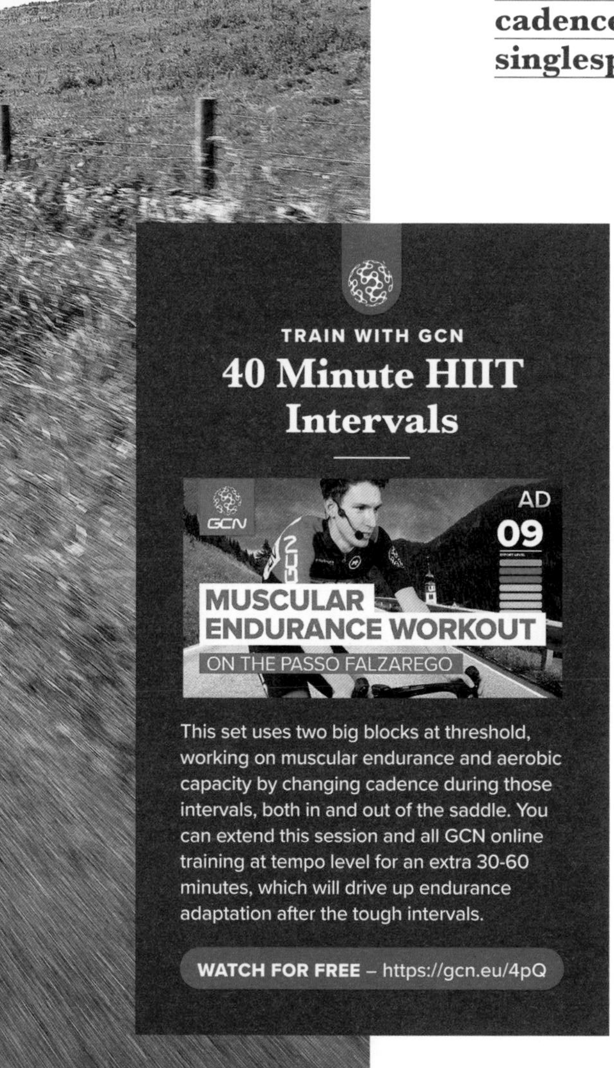

Power and cadence cessions

Power and cadence pyramids are good fun (read that as painful) to test all of the above. By increasing resistance every few minutes, you slow your cadence until you're pushing less than 60rpm in the saddle, grinding out your slowest-possible gear, before heading back up through the range, lightening the gear and increasing your cadence each time. In theory, you should be able to keep your power output the same because your higher cadence compensates for the loss in resistance. In practice, by the time you reach 110rpm, trying to put out the same power as when you were doing 60rpm is really tough.

Chapter Five

CORE & BODY CONDITIONING

Bolstering your foundations will increase endurance and cut injury risk

LP | **Cycling's time-consuming, but swapping a few miles for** strength and conditioning (S&C) exercises can lead to big gains. And the good news is that those who have little S&C history will typically see significant improvements over a short time period.

Conditioning exercises

Here's a five-exercise workout that takes little time and will help you avoid injury:

— **Leg lowers and neck holds**
Lie on your back. Bring both legs to 90 degrees at the hip. Control your back position as you breathe out and lower one leg. Hold for 30secs, change to other leg and complete four on each side. Progress to double-leg lower holds for 10secs x six, then to 30sec holds x two before moving onto 1min holds (fig 1).

— **Calf raises for Achilles**
On a single leg off the edge of a step, control rising on to the ball of your big toe over 2secs and then lower down over 4secs. Repeat, rising back up and controlling back down. Aim for 20 on each leg, three sets. Failing that, 10 reps and four sets.

— **Adductor holds for inner thigh**
This is a side plank with your top leg supported on a bench. You should start with your weight on your elbow directly under your shoulder, keeping chest forward. Drive the leg atop of the bench down into the bench to raise your hips. Once stable, elevate your lower leg off the floor and hold (fig 2). Aim for 30sec holds x four. Each side, two sets.

— **Side trunk holds for lateral trunk**
Hook your feet to lever off and support under your hips on a bench or Swiss ball. Keeping your body inline, use your trunk to lift your chest, keeping your body in a straight diagonal to your feet. As for your arms, start with them across your chest for holds, then progress to your arms reaching out (fig 3).

— **W-T-Ys – for back and shoulders**
Lying on your front, keep your stomach engaged and back flat with face looking down. Bring your shoulder blades back then elevate your wrists off the floor. Start in a W position, control out to a T, back to a W then reaching up to a Y. Repeat this sequence without rest for 1min and do three sets. Progress to adding a 1kg or 2kg weight in each hand (fig 4).

Fig 2

Fig 1

Fig 3

Fig 4

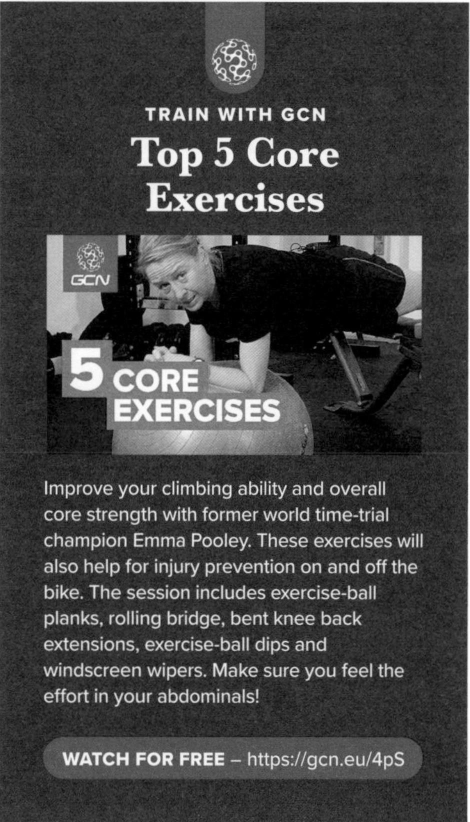

A hip flexor with rotation will crank up mobility on the bike

"Dynamic movements like those used in yoga encourage active mobility while working on your breathing"

Fig 1

Chapter Five

BOOST MOBILITY_

Increasing the range of motion in your joints will lead to the Holy Grail of riding – increased efficiency

LP | To stretch or not to stretch is the age-old debate. Having been a physio for 16 years, read the research and seen myriad variations, the conclusions aren't equivocal. What's more certain is that when we talk about mobility, we're looking to maintain optimal available range across the joints. You can see this in cycling when, for example, you're unravelling your body from the foetal position on the bike to returning to being upright and then walking.

That's why at least some of you will already engage in static stretching (where you hold a stretch in a static position). But the benefits of this form of popular stretching aren't conclusive with studies suggesting that for static stretching to work, it needs to be repeated every two hours, otherwise the tissues return to their original resting length.

Thankfully, there are many ways to skin (or should I say stretch!) a cat. Dynamic movements like those used in yoga, for example, encourage active mobility while working on breathing. Or work in the gym to load the tissues and create length change that lasts longer. Or undertake more off-the-bike movements and exercises that take you out of the position you've been in. For example, swimming to provide rotation and extension. Here are further examples that are easy to replicate at home and ticked off swiftly...

— **Hip flexor with rotation**
Split lunge with hand on the floor and chest rotation. Think about keeping your pelvis/hips level, push your back knee straight and rotate from your chest (fig 1).

— **Glutes stretch**
Also known as 'pigeon stretch' in yoga, moving from hands and knees, bring your left foot across and in front of your right knee, then slide the right leg back. If you can't hold your left shin parallel to the top of the mat, put support under your left knee to raise it off the floor and focus the stretch into your left glute.

— **Pec stretch**
Standing in your doorway, lift both elbows up and out against the doorframe, so your elbows are at the same level as your collar bones, then step your body through, bringing your chest forwards without arching your lower back. Keep breathing and, as you breathe out, slide your arms an inch higher up the doorway. You should feel a stretch across your chest and in your mid back. ⟶

Fig 2

Fig 3

— Quads stretch in kneeling
On one knee with your foot behind, tuck your pelvis under you, engaging the glutes on the side that you're stretching. Progress to reaching the arm on that side up to the ceiling (fig 2 and 3).

Fig 4

Fig 5

— Hamstring and calf active gliding with band
Lie face up on the floor with a resistance band around your foot. Keeping your thigh at 90 degrees, take your foot to the ceiling as you breathe out. Relax your knee as you breathe in. Repeat for 1min. Then hold the leg in the top range, before repeating the same at the ankle only, so pulling the toes to shin to ceiling as you breathe out. Relax your ankle as you breathe in (fig 4 and 5).

— Quads with a foam roller
Separate your quad into three sections, and sweep up and down with a foam roller six times. Hold on the tight points and, as you breathe out, bend your knee in and out to add a stretching component.

— Back rotation
Start in side-lying position and then, as you breathe out, rotate to open your chest out. Breathe in as you return your arm back to a side-lying position. Think about separating your shoulders as far as possible. If your knee's not remaining on the floor, add a foam roller or similar to support your knee (fig 6).

— Thoracic extension
Lying on your back with a peanut ball (two tennis balls wrapped together, inset pic) in-between your shoulder blades, open out your arms and slide the back of your hands along the floor to overhead. Return. Repeat for 1min at each level of your spine between the top and bottom of your shoulder blades (fig 7).

Fig 6

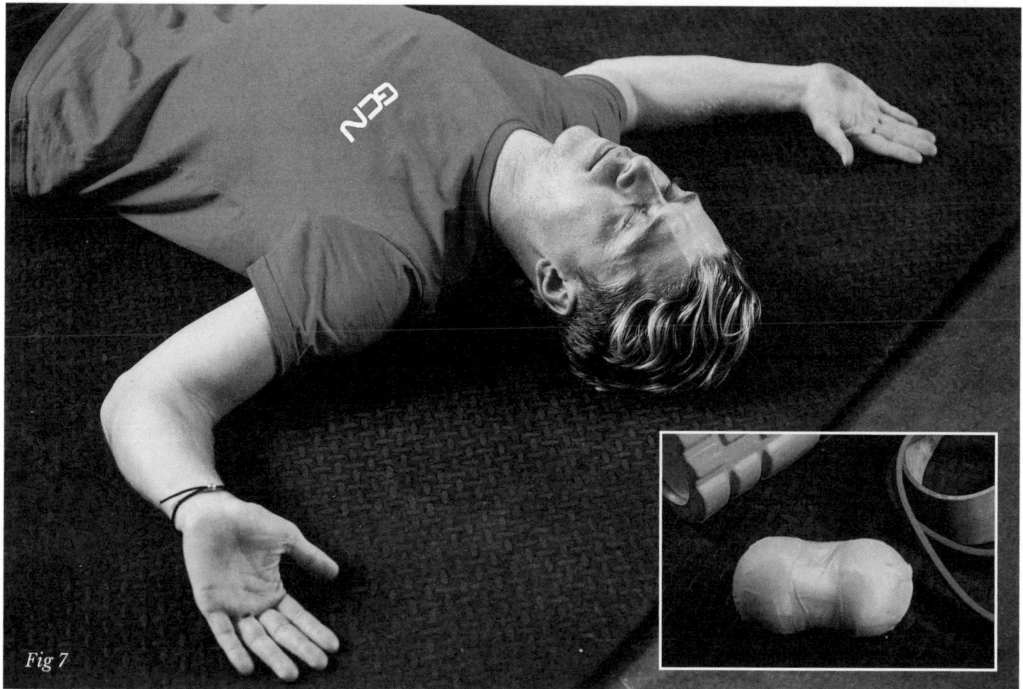

Fig 7

Chrissie Wellington broke all Ironman records in her relatively short pro career

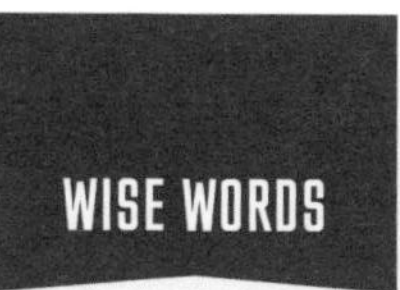

What Makes A Champion?

Chrissie Wellington is one of the greatest endurance athletes ever. Just what was Chrissie's secret?

ENDURANCE LESSONS WITH
Four-time Ironman world champion Chrissie Wellington

Chrissie Wellington OBE is a genuine contender for British sportsperson of the generation. She broke numerous long-course triathlon (3.8km swim, 180km bike, 42.2km run) records, remained unbeaten at Ironman and won the Ironman World Championship in Hawaii less than a year after turning professional before retiring in 2012.

Incredible – especially as Chrissie's training remained largely the same as it had been as an amateur. In other words, she kept things simple. Triathlon's a sport that typically attracts cutting-edge tech and the latest ideas on training. While Chrissie didn't ignore these advancements – using the latest aerodynamic gear, for example – her actual training relied heavily on perceived effort, listening to how her body felt.

This is a training principle encouraged by physiologist and collaborator to Chrissie's book, 'To The Finish Line', Dr Andrew Kirkland. Kirkland refers to the over-fixation on an athlete's technical measurements – their VO2 max, functional threshold power etc – and although these numbers have a place within sport, Andrew points out that the best possible measure for understanding physical capacity is the human brain. We understand how our performance is affected by our mood and life events in a way that a computer simply can't comprehend.

Though Chrissie changed little when turning professional, there were subtle but important tweaks, the main one around adopting a holistic approach to training. Her coach (Brett Sutton) told her early on, 'Physically →

"We understand how our performance is affected in a way that a computer simply can't comprehend"

WISE WORDS

you've got what it takes, but I'm going to have to chop your head off.' This meant embracing recovery and understanding that rest wasn't a sign of weakness. Her capacity to push beyond her limits wasn't the problem. But unbridled exertion needs discipline or it can result in more harm than good. She reflects that early on in her professional career, her instinct was to question everything – am I doing enough training? Am I doing enough races? With time and work she learnt to concentrate her energy on the task at hand.

You'd be forgiven for thinking that Chrissie is superhuman. But this is far from the truth. Pain, self-doubt and the sheer mental focus demanded by ultra-endurance affected her in the same way they do everyone. The reason she excelled over these obstacles is because she developed strategies. Countless hours in training taught her how to push past mental and physical barriers, buoyed by the knowledge that she's beaten them before and can do it again.

"She broke the race down into manageable chunks and relied on her capacity to dissociate to enter a more pleasurable headspace"

She broke the race down into manageable chunks and relied on her capacity to dissociate to enter a more pleasurable headspace. This included singing songs in her head, saying mantras – Chrissie was a big fan of Rudyard Kipling's poem 'If' – and counting numbers in time with her footfall. Whatever helped. It's critical that you develop these strategies in training. You can be fit as a fiddle but, if you haven't put in the mental preparation for an endurance race, you're at a disadvantage.

Outliers can be difficult case studies, not relatable as they operate on a seemingly unattainable plane. However, her ability to reflect on the pitfalls, hardships and transitions of her career is as impressive as any of her sporting attributes. There's no simple answer to the question, 'What makes a champion?' Every endurance athlete is different, trains differently and has a different motivation. But the ability to adapt and constantly move forward is something that unifies them all.

To hear more listen to the Endurance podcast on Apple Podcasts, Spotify, Google Podcasts, Amazon Music or search for it on your favourite podcast app.

Chrissie Wellington remained unbeaten at Ironman racing

Chapter Five

DO I NEED A COACH?

Outside input and an experienced sounding board may be what you need to reach your goals

MB | **I've learnt what I know organically, so have leant on** others to better inform this chapter. You don't know what you know as an athlete until you're asked to teach someone else. While I've not worked with a coach, I've been surrounded by different performance experts in my career, including Laura, who've helped to shape my training.

When I was 18 years old and went for my ski instructor's qualification, half of the course failed, not because they weren't great skiers, but because they struggled to learn how to do the basics again, how to break down what they knew in a way that could be understood. I'm aware of the same blind-spot as an endurance cyclist – I take for granted what I do naturally after decades of training and riding. Which is where a great coach comes in.

A coach is a valuable and interesting addition to your cycling performance, if you can afford the time and money to engage with someone who has relevant experience for what you're training for. I underline relevant as many ex-roadie racers who turn into cycling coaches will have no experience of endurance and adventure cycling.

Let's not create barriers to entry for endurance cycling – you can also build a huge amount of know-how yourself, from resources like this book and riding with friends.

Of course, you don't have to have a coach to become a brilliant endurance bike rider. But what coaches can bring is better accountability, structure and expertise, which is well worth the investment for many riders.

Round-the-world record-holder Jenny Graham explained to me the importance she places on her coach, as much for the psychological and mentoring help than the training schedules. Her coach had helped her get more out of training simply by talking through so many elements of her life off the bike.

"What coaches can bring is better accountability, structure and expertise, which is well worth the investment for many riders"

You should always look to learn and have fun, whether it's with friends or a coach

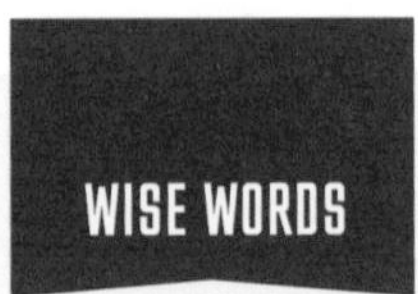

No More Tough Love

A coach can boost your motivation when spirits drop

ENDURANCE LESSONS WITH
Pav Bryan, performance director at Spokes

'Many of my clients say that they love working with me because I'm like a cheap therapist,' says Pav Bryan, performance director of Spokes, who specialise in training endurance athletes. Pav comments that though his clients might be adept at spotting the physical warning signs of fatigue, they often fail to acknowledge the mental symptoms. Building a rapport with an athlete enables him to notice the changes in their tone or manner that indicates a lack of recovery. This could be because of their training schedule, sleep quality or inadequate nutrition.

Over time a coach recognises what type of training their athlete responds to best and can design a bespoke programme accordingly. What kind of intensity do they need? What sequencing works best? Do they respond to linear or reverse periodisation? Finding the answers to these questions is a process that takes time, but one that yields substantial results.

Coaching is much more complicated than a set of quantitative measurements can reveal. Yes, there's a place for knowing your functional threshold power, heart rate etc. But Pav estimates that training only contributes 15% to an athlete's overall gains. Around 35% is attributable to nutrition and a whopping 50% comes from the athlete's mental approach. People break mentally, losing interest or motivation, far quicker than they do physically. It's easy to become lured into a training frenzy by the initial spike in performance indicators, but riders are left reeling when they have their first setback. Many amateurs lose interest after they struggle in their first event or begin to stagnate in training. Enthusiasm is essential for success in sport but the best results are always gained from a measured approach.

To hear more, listen to the Endurance podcast on Apple Podcasts, Spotify, Google Podcasts, Amazon Music or search for it on your favourite podcast app.

Your team – forging memories that'll last way beyond the end of your challenge

Chapter Five

FINAL THOUGHTS

A summary of training, strength and stamina advice to take away to your bike

For endurance cyclists, the longer you can build up and the more conditioning you train as a rider, the more you'll be able to endure and enjoy those longer rides. Cue chapter reflection...

Conditioned to Succeed

The following issues often prevent the success of your endurance event and are fixed by strength and conditioning, rather than just more cycling: the neck and spine are under strain and will need muscular support; the hips can cause issues from being in a sustained deep-flex position; and there's also potentially going to be problems with tendinopathy around the ankle and knee.

Slow Progress, Big Rewards

Most injuries happen when you have a big jump in intensity or duration of riding. If you do have such a transition point – for example, between training and the endurance event itself – then be aware of inflammation or irritation. Be ready to treat with ice and elevation, but also do everything you can to minimise the jump.

Copy Challenge Conditions

If your event starts early in the morning or goes through the night, do some training sessions at those times simply to challenge your body clock and alertness, as well as to practise fuelling at odd times of the day.

Core Strength

Your tummy seemingly enjoys an easy ride when cycling. It doesn't. A strong core, especially when climbing, will give you so much better positioning and fluidity on the bike. So do 10 minutes' core exercises every day.

Stretch and Endure

Endurance cycling can give you a similar hunch as being draped over a laptop for too long – Thoracic Kyphosis, to give it its proper term. This explains why I was a few centimetres shorter after cycling around the world – until I opened up my chest and remembered how to stand upright again, that is. Pectoral stretch in a doorway so you don't get stuck in the endurance hunch. People will just think that you like hanging around!

"A strong core, especially when climbing, will give you so much better positioning and fluidity on the bike"

Replace a modicum of cycling with core efforts to ride stronger

Chapter Six

FUELLING FOR ENDURANCE

The right food maximises training adaptations, boosts immunity and lifts your mood. And, praise be, food can be delicious as well as nutritious

You wouldn't fuel a Ferrari on second-rate fuel, so don't do the same with your own engine

Chapter Six

FOOD FOR THOUGHT

The final piece of the endurance jigsaw is the tastiest. Time to chow down on cycling nutrition

MB | **The purpose of this chapter is to share my experience of** nutrition and hydration when endurance riding, and signpost some of the pitfalls I've endured along the way.

As an endurance athlete, I've always considered myself a 'diesel engine' so fuel accordingly. What you put in your mouth affects your mood and motivation to ride, so you must be conscious of ironing out the psychological peaks and troughs of sugar and caffeine as much as possible. Like most cyclists, I love a good coffee and have a sweet tooth, so I'm not suggesting being a purist – I'm simply promoting self-awareness and, where possible, moderation.

When calculating your fuelling routine, hydration's often overlooked. In basic terms, I normally ride with one bottle of water and the other with an electrolyte in it, but that changes depending on climate. Drinking's a habit and even professional cyclists mess up regularly, especially in the cold.

Little and often

The golden rule of nutrition and hydration is to eat and drink before you're hungry and thirsty, little and often. Leave it until your body's alarm bells ring and it's too late – and it's incredibly hard to play catch-up. Remember that nutrition and hydration aren't just crucial to get you through an endurance ride, but to pre-empt and aid the recovery so you can get up and go again the next day. Be under no illusions – nutrition will make as big a difference to your endurance riding as training will.

"Be under no illusions – nutrition will make as big a difference to your endurance riding as training will"

I'm from the 'natural school of nutrition', meaning I'd prefer a wrap or banana over a gel or a sports bar; that said, commercial energy products do have their place. As for diet, I've not stuck to any particular one. I've been plant based, vegetarian, an omnivore – sometimes through choice, sometimes through necessity on my expeditions. Ultimately, you can be a high-performing endurance athlete on a wide variety of diets.

Chapter Six

GET THE BASICS RIGHT FIRST

Lay the nutritional foundations and you'll enjoy a stronger base on which to apply the marginal wins

LP | **Even if we lay in bed for 24 hours, our bodies would still** require energy to keep our bodily systems functioning. For the average male, this is around 1,800kcals a day; for the average female, 1,500kcals. Throw in exercise and, of course, this energy demand increases.

There's a minefield of information when it comes to fuelling, including the theory of marginal gains, popularised by Sir Dave Brailsford, British Cycling and Team Sky. It's proven at elite level but, at recreational level, this means people end up focussing on the smaller things at the cost of ensuring the foundations are in place. The BIG gains are in getting the basics right. Sort those and marginal gains come into play. For instance, if you're consuming a cherry shot prior to cycling in search of a micronutrient boost, but you're not getting your five-a-day, it'll do nothing.

Working on foundations may not sound like the silver bullet, but it's where everyone needs to start. So, this chapter will focus on the importance of fuelling foundations, what they are and how to address them. Only towards the end will we explore the world of supplements and specific diets – but I urge you to not skip to the end for the shiny adjuncts.

Energy Systems

When we talk about training and fuelling, it isn't as binary as switching one system off and another on, says the English Institute of Sport's Rich Burden. It is, however, useful to know how your different energy systems contribute to your training and rides of different intensities.

The phosphagen system (ATP-PCr)
Your body breaks down ATP (adenosine triphosphate) to fuel movement of all types. Phosphocreatine (PCr) is used to resynthesise ATP to provide a rapid source of energy during highly intense exercise, lasting approximately 10-30 seconds.

The glycolytic system
Uses carbohydrate to produce ATP to support increasing durations, lasting 30 seconds to three minutes. During a long ride, when you hit a hill or need to put the hammer down this is what you draw on. When people talk about the **anaerobic system**, this simply means oxygen isn't involved as an energy source, which includes both phosphagen and glycolytic systems.

The aerobic system
Uses oxygen to help with energy production, generating energy from carbohydrate, fat and protein. The aerobic system creates ATP less rapidly than the phosphagen and glycolytic systems but provides a much larger source to fuel the long-duration, steady-state rides.

Don't fall into the fad-diet trap. It might sound dull but simple and proven is best

Macronutrients, like carbs from rice pudding and jam, are just one part of the fuelling equation

Chapter Six

THE HUMAN MACHINE

Your mix of macronutrients and micronutrients is a huge driver of health and performance

MB | **Many coaches and sports nutritionists use the engine** analogy to explain that macronutrients are your petrol (drive), but you also need micronutrients that are your oil (efficiency). If you don't look after the micronutrients, your engine simply doesn't last as long or run as efficiently. Focus on these as much as you focus on macronutrients (the petrol).

"While macronutrients are responsible for the drive, micronutrients take care of the drive's efficiency"

Macronutrients are responsible for the drive. They're made up of carbohydrates, fats and protein with each providing energy in different amounts by weight. Carbohydrates and protein provide around four calories per gramme, while fat delivers around nine calories per gramme.

Carbohydrates and fats are the primary sources of energy, albeit protein's energy potential can be tapped into if the body's fasting or starving. This is rare and not ideal as this is a situation when the body will begin breaking down muscle.

While macronutrients are responsible for the drive, micronutrients take care of the efficiency of the drive. They're made up of vitamins, minerals, antioxidants and phytonutrients, often sourced from colourful fruit and vegetables.

Balance the petrol and oil!

Eating a high-calorie but low-nutrient diet is like having a high fuel-to-oil ratio. Your engine will run, but not efficiently, and will eventually encounter problems. Aside from being a better endurance bike rider, this relates to your longevity and ability to avoid illness throughout your life. Swap excess petrol consumption (macronutrients) with more oil (micronutrients) to increase your chances of a longer, healthier life.

As you've seen from the macronutrient breakdown, not all calories are equal. Our bodies process healthy and unhealthy foods differently. Calorie counting alone simply doesn't work, as 100kcals of chocolate and 100kcals of fruit and veg elicit different effects on your body, which is where the value of micronutrients come in.

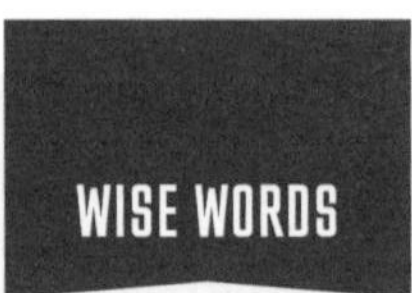

Eat The Good Stuff

An award-winning cyclist and chef on making your culinary life simple and effective

ENDURANCE LESSONS WITH
Michelin-starred chef and world duathlon champion Alan Murchison

As an endurance athlete, it's possible to be lean, light and extremely unhealthy. The analogy that Alan uses is, 'If you were driving from Edinburgh to London, would you start that journey with a quarter of a tank of fuel? No way. And if you were going down the road to the shops you wouldn't put 80 quid's worth of diesel in the car.'

The solution? Know what's in your food. If you can see on the back of a protein bar that it's packed with chemicals, it's not good for your body. That's not to say that bars, shakes and gels don't have their place, but that when you put something unknown into your system you take a risk. Cooking from scratch allows you to enjoy greater benefits, for about 20 percent of the price, and with much tastier results. How? Go simple. Transport yourself back to your granny's house and think about that wholesome, hearty and humble food that'd satisfy the most pompous of food critics. We're talking flapjacks, soups, pastas and slow-cooked chicken.

Cooking isn't high up on the agenda of most athletes. It takes time, money and a bit of know-how. But as well as his delicious recipes, which can be found in his book *'The Cycling Chef'*, Alan has tips to make cooking easier. Firstly, use your rest day to cook in batches, planning your meals like you would your training and prep ahead. When he's on the bike, he packs flapjacks, oat bars with dates and sweet-potato brownies. Yum! That said, some people can't stomach solids when cycling so find out what works for you. Just remember: it doesn't need to be scientific or gourmet. Keep it simple, keep it relevant for your needs and always ask yourself: 'What would my granny say?'

To hear more listen to the Endurance podcast on Apple Podcasts, Spotify, Google Podcasts, Amazon Music or search for it on your favourite podcast app.

Commercial bars and gels have their place but you can't beat going natural

A long day in the saddle's that bit more comfortable if your stomach's happy

Chapter Six

FUELLING FOR EVENTS

Key strategies to ride strong and avoid the bonk

MB | **On days when you're racking up endurance miles or the main** event itself, breaking the overnight fast is essential. You must eat a good breakfast, no matter how nerves might be killing your appetite, otherwise you're heading for a bonk even before you mount your bike. A pre-endurance-ride breakfast could be porridge and a protein shake – plant-based if vegan – or some eggs.

Experiment with both food and hydration in training, so there's nothing new on event day. Your stomach works differently under the strain of endurance, so be kind to it. Bring plenty of ride foods and eat small amounts often. Start eating and sipping within 30 minutes of the start to forge good habits.

When indoor training, drink within the first 10 minutes when you experience the biggest change in body temperature. If competing in an organised sportive, be careful to not get carried away with what's on offer at their fuelling stations. Stick to what's familiar and avoid overdosing on sugary snacks and drinks.

Don't wait until you bonk

It's hard to recover if you only start eating and drinking when you start to bonk. If you run out of energy, the symptoms include heavy legs, a light head, a cold sweat, blurry vision and an inability to raise effort levels. Your tank's running on empty so reach for fast-acting sugars and carbs before building back slower-burning carbs and fats.

Whether doing a single day endurance ride, or a multi-day event, or any kind of training in the build-up, your post-ride routine is key to starting the recovery process. Within 20 minutes, eat and/or drink something that contains protein for rebuilding and carbohydrates to restock energy stores. Carb uptake is at its highest straight after riding.

"Your stomach works differently under the strain of endurance, so be kind to it"

Your nutrition plan

Eating well is as much about organisation as anything else. 10 minutes of prep before leaving the house can solve poor eating choices most of the time when out and about. The following options were given to Mark in the build- →

up to his 18,000-mile ride. Bear in mind this was during a full-time training schedule, so would be varied in quantities depending on the load that day and week.

— BREAKFAST OPTIONS —

60g porridge with semi-skimmed milk with one tablespoon seeds; large handful of berries or other brightly coloured fruit. Add two tablespoons of natural yoghurt.

—

Two scrambled, poached or boiled eggs, or beans, on two medium-slices of toast; one wholemeal bagel and thin spread of choice followed by large fruit – kiwi, orange, mango etc.

—

30g fruit-and-fibre cereal plus one Weetabix with milk. 150g yoghurt and a large handful of berries or mango.

—

500ml water/electrolytes to start the day plus tea or coffee as you wish.

— SNACK OPTIONS —

Tupperware box of mixed-whole nuts and seeds – large handful for a portion.

—

Tupperware box of dried fruit – small handful a portion.

—

Packs of flapjack.

—

Pack of healthy granola.

—

Healthier nut spreads on bread.

—

150g of berries or a fresh piece of fruit, or cereal bars – less processed ones.

—

300g natural dairy yoghurt with 150g seasonal berries.

—

500ml milk and small banana.

— LUNCH OPTIONS —

Carbs: either one large wrap, rice, pasta, sweet or regular potato with protein: fish, meat (not processed such as ham), eggs, cottage cheese; lots of colour, i.e. two large handfuls of spinach leaves or rocket salad or other leafy salad greens and carrot, tomatoes or beetroot; small amount of oil for dressing.

—

One large piece of fruit.

— DINNER OPTIONS —

Include lots of colourful vegetables.

—

Protein – regular fillet of meat or fish, or two eggs, or large portion of beans or pulses.

—

Carbs – 85g dried-weight pasta or rice or regular potato or sweet potato.

— SUPPER OPTIONS —

Two large fruit chopped with 150g yoghurt.

—

Two oatcakes with cottage cheese and chopped apple.

Taken from the training phase of 'Around the World in 80 Days' by Ruth McKean, performance nutritionist for Mark Beaumont, now the performance dietician for the British Skeleton Team

Eggs provide a rich source of protein, while avocado's great for good fats

Chapter Six

SWEETS & BOOZE

When it comes to treats, stick to the 80:20 rule and you'll keep trim and ride strong

MB | **Some simple psychology – when it comes to healthy nutrition,** focus all conversations and planning on what you can eat rather than what you shouldn't. Talking about the 'forbidden fruits' makes it hard in the long term to forge new habits.

Amateur athletes, juggling family and work lives, should use the 80/20 rule, where you can still enjoy your treats, but bear in mind that it's what you do 80% of the time that matters the most. Snacks, especially saturated fat and sugar, as well as alcohol, are likely to be the 20%. You don't need to plan the 20%, as long as you have focussed your plan on the 80%.

"Enjoy your treats, but bear in mind that it's what you do 80% of the time that matters the most"

— Sugar

Foods that are high in sugar cause our glucose levels to spike, which results in more insulin being secreted – a hormone responsible for moving glucose out of the bloodstream. Losing body fat is difficult with high levels of insulin present, as it's a storage hormone.

— Alcohol

Alcohol blocks our ability to break down energy from macronutrients. So, put simply, anything we eat while drinking alcohol is stored. Moderate drinking is one or two drinks per day for healthy women or men, depending on your size. However, we all react to alcohol differently.

— Myth-busting

Evidence that drinking red wine, in particular, can help avoid heart disease is pretty weak. All of the research showing that people drinking moderate amounts of alcohol have lower rates of heart disease is observational. Such studies can't prove cause and effect, only association.

Similarly, there's a thought that beer's good for carbohydrates and electrolytes. I'm afraid not. While a beer post-workout isn't hugely detrimental as long as it's taken with water and food, it's certainly not beneficial to cycling performance. Beer and any alcohol is dehydrating, which will extend the recovery period and lessen fitness gains.

All that said, the social side of cycling is important – just don't overdo it. Cheers!

Focus your planning on the 80% healthy choices. The 20% – the treats – will take care of themselves

Electrolyte drinks are a proven strategy to rehydrate proficiently. They add taste too

Chapter Six

HYDRATION MATTERS

Your body and brain need constant hydrating to perform at their optimum

LP | **Hydration's often overlooked, in particular the impact it has** on cognition and mood as well as our fundamental survival. We tend to prioritise food but our body's hierarchy of needs is that we can only last three days without water, but we can last up to three weeks without food.

When we lack energy, suffer a drop in decision-making abilities or endure a change in mood, we tend to reach for food before hydration. But our bodies need fluid for our brain to function; to support nerve conduction; for our circulation to flow; for our bodies to heal and fight infections; to lubricate the joints and much more. For basics, such as breathing, kidney function and sweating, we can lose two litres of fluid each day.

"We can only last three days without water, but we can last up to three weeks without food"

This doesn't include the impact of the environment (heat/humidity/altitude) nor physical exertion.

Cues for drinking are largely based around thirst but, by the time you're thirsty, you're already over 2% dehydrated. Yes, you can survive on little fluid per day, but significant research* has shown that just a 2% drop in hydration has a significant impact on performance.

Optimum hydration

There's a big difference in reaching the minimum hydration levels required to survive versus what's required to perform optimally. With Mark, it wasn't until we did a sweat test with him where he saw that he lost nearly two litres of fluid in one hour on the bike (in a heated chamber), which made Mark realise how he'd become used to riding dehydrated.

One of the annoyances when adequately hydrating during a ride is that inevitably it increases the need to go for a wee and, therefore, leads to regular stops. However, your kidneys are like your gut – you need to train them to adapt. If you drip-feed in the fluids regularly and often – 10ml every 10 minutes – then it allows the gut time to absorb, rather than downing a one litre in one go. Also, consider that a normal urine →

**Neil P Walsh (2018). Review: Recommendations to maintain immune health in athletes. European Journal of Sport Science. Vol. 18, No. 6, 820–831, https://doi.org/10.1080/17461391.2018.1449895*

"By understanding the specifics of a cyclist's fluid and salt loss, you can form an accurate replacement plan"

output if you're hydrated should be about six times a day. If you're only going twice a day, you're in a chronic state of dehydration.

When to use electrolytes

When we sweat, it tastes salty. These 'salts' are a combination of sodium, chloride, potassium, magnesium and calcium. For an athlete, we often test both sweat rate and sweat concentration. By understanding the specifics of an individual's fluid and salt loss, you can start to form an accurate fluid-replacement plan.

However, we don't all have the luxury of a lab to provide specific data, but there are some simple measures we can take to understand our sweat rate.

Weigh yourself immediately pre- and post-bike session on a set of scales, ideally naked. If in an hour you've lost 1kg without having gone to the loo, this correlates to a loss of around one litre of fluid. If you've consumed one litre of fluid during that hour, then you need to add this to the loss, so therefore two litres of fluid loss in an hour. There are a number of variables that can impact this. Environmental temperature is a key one. But this method provides a solid template from which to build your fluid-replacement plan.

Electrolyte drinks are not only there for replacement of salts lost – sodium and glucose work together to aid absorption of water. The sodium and glucose co-transport system draws water across the membrane via a method of osmosis on a 1:1 ratio basis of sodium to glucose in the small intestine. Choose a quality electrolyte, from a reputable sports brand, rather than sugary versions made by soft drink companies. Ensure you look beyond the marketing and analyse the ingredient list.

When considering the use of electrolytes, start with a 500-750ml drink every four hours during long-duration exercise. If high intensity and short duration in hot climates, then an electrolyte drink prior- and post-exercise is useful, too.

Of course, sweat rate and concentration will vary depending on exercise intensity, duration, environmental heat, body composition, nutrition, hydration and age, so if you're looking to gain further specificity, then seek the expertise of a physiologist with a laboratory to ascertain more accurate personalised hydration strategies.*

**Kelly A. Barnes, Melissa L. Anderson, John R. Stofan, Kortney J. Dalrymple, Adam J. Reimel, Timothy J. Roberts, Rebecca K. Randell, Corey T. Ungaro & Lindsay B. Baker (2019): Normative data for sweating rate, sweat sodium concentration, and sweat sodium loss in athletes: An update and analysis by sport, Journal of Sports Sciences.*

Undertaking a simple sweat test will help you to determine how much drink you need each hour

Longer rides should comprise more than just energy products to prevent 'gut disturbance'

Chapter Six

GOING WITH YOUR GUT

A cyclist marches (rides) on their stomach. That's why you must treat it with love, respect and probiotics

LP | **When entering the world of endurance, spend time** understanding what your gut responds to, ensuring it'll cope with different types of fuelling and how it responds at different stages of fatigue. As many endurance cyclists will testify, it's often their stomach and not their legs that let them down.

As an example, do you know how your gut responds to caffeine during exercise? Is your gut able to digest nuts and seeds or does it make you bloated? Do you get taste fatigue or loss of appetite after riding for more than six hours?

On rides that are in excess of six hours, you must ensure your fuelling's made up of more than gels, bars or acidic drinks. When you rely solely on sugary-based fuels for a long period of time, you can cause gut disturbance because you've made your stomach too acidic by changing the resting pH. This drop in your gut pH will no longer maintain a good environment for the healthy bacteria; instead, it'll be optimal for the bad bacteria to thrive. A number of supplements now provide electrolyte or carb-based drinks that are neutral pH so they don't affect gut acidity.

When preparing for big events or rides in different countries where food sources may be hard to find, unfamiliar or have questionable food hygiene, it's important that you work on gut resilience. This means that months out from your event, build up your gut microbiome – the army in your stomach – to be as varied and robust as possible to minimise risk of gut illness.

Look after the good bacteria

Our gut is home to an array of bacteria and enzymes that assist in breaking down foods, absorbing the nutrients and protecting us from harmful bacteria or viruses that may be ingested through foods or fluids.

In the gut we have healthy bacteria, which aids our immunity through →

"Build up your gut microbiome – the army in your stomach – to be as varied and robust as possible to minimise risk of gut illness"

"Prebiotics are foods that healthy bacteria live off, so are useful at keeping the healthy bacteria active"

improving our absorption of nutrients and helps to resist harmful bacteria that enters the system. So we can boost the healthy bacteria found naturally in certain types of food like live yoghurts, and fermented or pickled vegetables such as sauerkraut or miso soup. These are classed as natural probiotics. You can also add probiotics in the form of supplementation.

Prebiotics are foods that healthy bacteria live off, so are equally as useful at keeping the healthy bacteria active in the gut. Some natural food sources of prebiotics are chicory root, garlic, Jerusalem artichoke, leeks, asparagus, barley, oats, apples and bananas, to name just a few.

Focus on good hygiene

For Mark's 80 Days, gut illness was the highest risk on the list to impact time lost. It meant that Ruth McKean, his nutritionist, worked on various supplementation and meal-planning suggestions six months out from the start. During the 80 Days, I supplemented him with a daily probiotic. Our food-hygiene processes in the van were also extremely diligent. We avoided all processed meats, only ate vegetables and fruits we could peel or cook, and ensured any refrigerated foods were stored at the right temperature. It worked as he remained 'gut strong'!

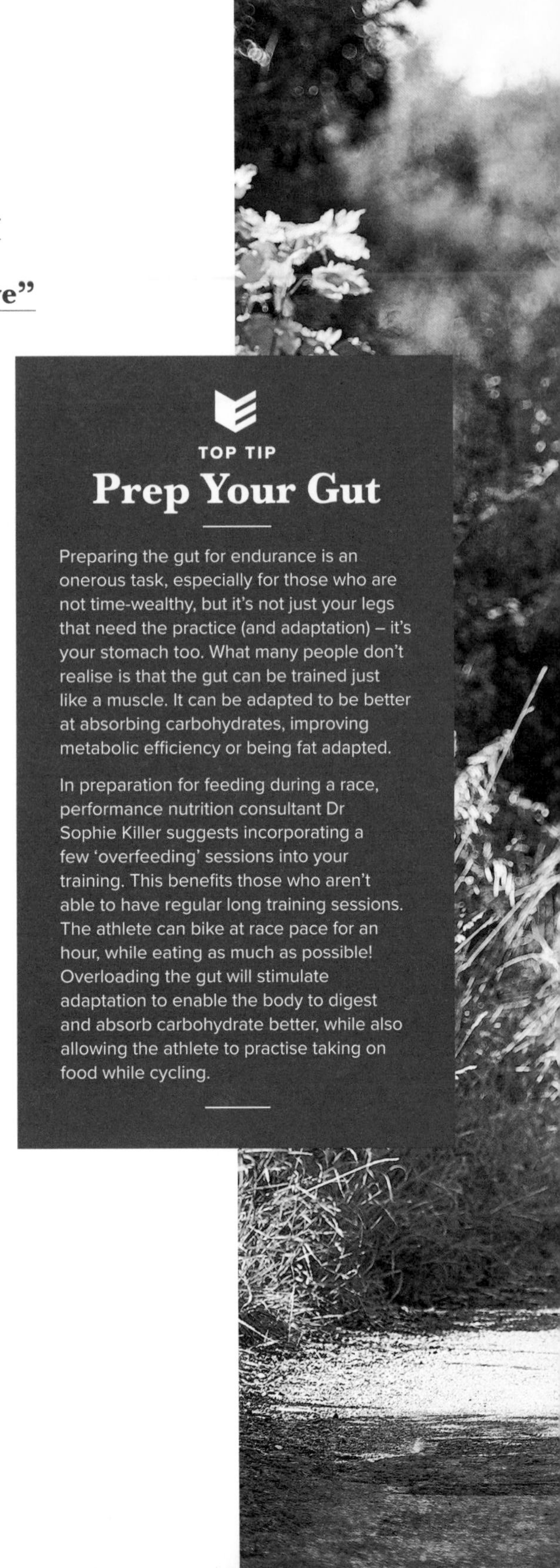

TOP TIP

Prep Your Gut

Preparing the gut for endurance is an onerous task, especially for those who are not time-wealthy, but it's not just your legs that need the practice (and adaptation) – it's your stomach too. What many people don't realise is that the gut can be trained just like a muscle. It can be adapted to be better at absorbing carbohydrates, improving metabolic efficiency or being fat adapted.

In preparation for feeding during a race, performance nutrition consultant Dr Sophie Killer suggests incorporating a few 'overfeeding' sessions into your training. This benefits those who aren't able to have regular long training sessions. The athlete can bike at race pace for an hour, while eating as much as possible! Overloading the gut will stimulate adaptation to enable the body to digest and absorb carbohydrate better, while also allowing the athlete to practise taking on food while cycling.

Your gut's under similar pressure to your heart, lungs and muscles so treat it with the utmost respect

Eating a well-balanced and healthy diet is a key ingredient of a strong immune system

Chapter Six

BOOSTING IMMUNITY_

Remaining strong and healthy in life and on two wheels will keep you on track to achieve your aims

LP | **A threat to physical performance in sport is a compromised** immune system, leading to illnesses like upper respiratory tract infections (URTI), also known as the common cold. Key factors that impact our immunity are heavy exercise, psychological stress, nutritional deficits, sleep disruption, environmental temperature extremes, altitude and long-haul travel. If you're falling ill repeatedly, consider why and look at the following:

— Hygiene routines (how thorough are you with washing your hands and staying distant from others with colds? Covid-19 processes are only enforcing proper hygiene routines).
— Training load.
— Fuelling around training.
— Recovery and sleep.
— Work stress.
— Home/family environment.
— Other health concerns, which mean your immunity is compromised.

Identifying a possible causal factor can mean being more targeted in your approach. There's no point taking extra supplements when what you need is an extra hour's sleep. If you know the cause and it's not something you can change or influence, there are things to build your defensive wall before it's attacked:

— A well-balanced diet.
— Increasing to nine portions of fruit and veg daily.
— Frequent intake of protein sources throughout the day, from breakfast through to a shake prior to bed.
— Staying well hydrated.
— Ensuring adequate recovery time.

If you're doing the above but getting repeated colds, consider the following:

— See your GP to make sure there isn't anything medical underlying.
— Ask your GP to check vitamin D and ferritin levels.
— Increasing natural antioxidants such as berries, green tea and dark chocolate.
— Drinking hot water with fresh lemon, fresh ginger and Manuka honey regularly.
— Consider a probiotic supplement (≥1,010 live bacteria/day).
— At the onset of a cold, consider zinc acetate lozenges (75 mg/day) and vitamin C (RDA 75 mg/day for females and 90 mg/day for males)*.

**NEIL P. WALSH (2018) REVIEW: Recommendations to maintain immune health in athletes. European Journal of Sport Science. Vol. 18, No. 6, 820–831, https://doi.org/10.1080/17461391.2018.1449895*

Chapter Six

A WEIGHTY TOPIC

Weight's a sensitive issue for both male and female cyclists. Just remember, we're all unique

MB | **Given the choice, I'd prefer to not talk about weight loss for all** of its negative connotations around diets. However, discussions about power-to-weight ratio mean the topic is unavoidable. So I'd suggest the following context to any such discussion – I want to encourage everyone, regardless of shape and size, to get out and ride. We can all enjoy cycling and we can all endure.

"The best way to lose weight isn't necessarily through more training but dietary choices"

I'm 6ft 3in tall and about 90kg. That's no Tour de France anatomy. But that's not to say that I haven't focussed on my nutrition as an athlete, not least because I have a sweet tooth and like the odd beer. But the image of rake-thin cyclists stems from racing cyclists, whose build is more like Chris Froome – which the vast majority of us are not! So be careful not to pass even casual comments about body and weight unless you know someone well, as you have no idea what life-long internal conversations people face with their physical image and their relationship with food. It's important to keep nutritional conversations positive and focussed on the changes you wish to see, rather than the problems that you perceive.

About you, not anyone else

If you wish to change your own weight, do it based on the way it makes you feel and your efficiency on the bike, not as a comparison to others. Like any training gains, make it personal and make your wins about your personal best, rather than comparative success. Your happiness and mental health are at the heart of your ability to ride consistently.

Given this important context, being lighter does make cycling uphill easier – thank you gravity!

Put simply, it's easier to eat than it is to burn this off. Weight gain is often a higher energy intake compared to output and it's easy to underestimate how energy-dense foods can be, and often overestimate how much energy you actually burn during exercise.

You can easily eat 1,000kcals within 10 minutes, but it'd likely take a few hours of exercise to burn this off. The best way to lose weight isn't necessarily through training more, but through portion control and dietary choices.

Your happiness and mental health are at the heart of good cycling

Fiona Kolbinger fuelled optimally on her way to winning the Transcontinental Race

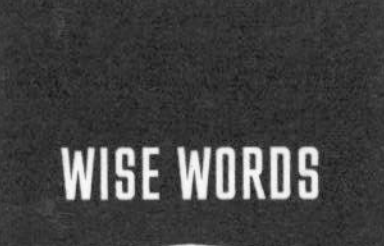

Relative Energy Deficiency In Sport & Fasted Sessions

Playing around with your energy intake can prove beneficial, but beware of the dangers

ENDURANCE LESSONS WITH
Elite performance consultant **Dr Sophie Killer** and high-performance dietician **Rebecca Dent**

Relative Energy Deficiency in Sport (aka REDS) is a fairly common occurrence in endurance sports, where very low body-fat levels are often considered key to athletic success. To achieve this, many athletes will under-fuel over long periods of time, operating in an energy deficit, which is ultimately deleterious for their health. Previously referred to as the 'Female Athlete Triad', a condition defined by a lack of menstrual cycle, disordered eating and/or poor bone mineral density, the updated theory extends beyond these three criteria. REDS reflects that this is a condition that can also be experienced by male athletes. In addition to the symptoms of the Female Athlete Triad, REDS includes a wide range of negative outcomes such as disrupted sleep quality, negative mood disturbance, increased risk of injury and, ultimately, decreased training response and reduced performance (impacting both endurance and strength).

How to avoid REDS

Sophie uses several strategies to help athletes achieve their optimal body composition while avoiding REDS. One is completing all key training sessions in an environment of 'high-energy availability'; in other words, making sure you have fuel in the tank! If you're training hard, you don't want to put additional stress on your body by withholding the energy that it needs. Exercising in a fasted state, for →

"REDS includes a range of negative outcomes such as disrupted sleep and increased risk of injury"

WISE WORDS

"You're most likely to get a PB when you have fuel in the tank, which shouldn't come as any surprise"

instance, causes cortisol to remain elevated in the blood after training. Cortisol is a stress hormone and is naturally produced during exercise. However, it typically drops to baseline shortly after exercise has finished. If you haven't eaten anything, it stays elevated for a longer period, which can have an impact on the immune system and your ability to recover.

Match your training needs

Training with 'high energy availability' – in other words, having the right nutrients in your pre-training meal and fuelling during prolonged exercise – can help to protect our bodies. You're most likely to produce a PB when you have fuel in the tank, which shouldn't come as any surprise.

Having less energy when we don't need it but protecting our training sessions with high energy availability when we do need it can work well for a lot of athletes in terms of optimising body composition and performance in the long run. If you want to cut the carbs, go ahead, but periodise this in line with training and make sure that you surround your key training sessions with the energy your body needs.

The appeal of fasted exercise is that it encourages fat adaptation, meaning that your body has started to burn fat instead of carbs. Rebecca points out that high-volume, low-intensity training, regardless of dietary intake, enhances the body's capacity to use fat as a resource. Fasted sessions can be done safely, but they must be introduced gradually and with a specific purpose. As already discussed, fasting compounds the stress on your body in addition to the stress already caused by exercise. As a result, it'll increase fatigue and recovery time.

If you're intending on fasted exercise, ensure that you do so in moderation and leave ample time for recovery. Also, introduce fasted sessions at the right time. Don't put them next to strength training or higher-intensity sessions, like hills, intervals or speed sessions because you'll underperform and lower your immune system. And don't jump in too soon – build up over a series of weeks, half an hour, an hour and so on.

To hear more listen to the Endurance podcast on Apple Podcasts, Spotify, Google Podcasts, Amazon Music or search for it on your favourite podcast app.

Fasted sessions, actioned carefully, can work, but 'filling the tank' is the general aim

Planning and prepping your nutrition will result in better-quality fuelling

Chapter Six

FINAL THOUGHTS

Nail your nutrition and you'll serve up an endurance ride you can be proud of

We've taken you on quite a journey and there's much to digest. But here's a brief reflection on the past chapter.

Survival vs Performance

You can survive just three days without water, eight days without sleep and up to three weeks without food. This shows how important these three elements are for function, so they should be a high priority when it comes to performance.

Be Prepared

Learn to cook the basics and plan ahead for training rides so you know what breakfast and meals you'll have that day and what snacks you'll take on the bike.

Get Your Antioxidants

Eat a minimum of five fruit and veg portions a day, increasing to eight to nine portions to reduce risk of illness.

Supplement Your Riding

Supplements to consider are: probiotics, omega-3 and multivitamin; zinc lozenges at early signs of a cold; pH-neutral carb drinks or gels; and electrolyte drinks to optimise water absorption.

GCN
GLOBAL CYCLING NETWORK